The Bookplates of Miss C. Helard

and other related matters

Percy Thomas

The Bookplates of
Miss C. Helard

and other related matters

Colin R. Lattimore

The Bookplate Society

2012

Dedicated to
my grandchildren, Emily, Katie, James
and Alice

'*Many things our grandfathers knew*
are lost to us and our grandchildren will
search in vain for things which to us
are most familiar.'

Anonymous quotation favoured by
Arthur Charles Fox-Davies

Contents

(*Frontispiece*) Fig. 1 Etching of Miss C. Helard by Percy Thomas, undertaken whilst she was his student in 1900 – Artist's presentation copy to the sitter, inscribed 'Percy Thomas – with kind regards to Miss Helard'

(*Title page*) H095, 1917, Lady (Dorothea) Wharton

(*Front cover*) H099, 1922, Henry George Charles, Viscount Lascelles

(*Back cover*) Original drawings by C. Helard showing four Royal Badges – 'Crowned Portcullis', 'The Rose-en-Soleil', 'The Sun Burst' and 'Rose and Pomegranate'

Illustrations

Acknowledgements

The writing of a book is never a single-handed exercise and this volume is no exception. I am indebted to many people in various ways, for help and support, but in particular to the following:

Colonel Tony Molesworth for giving me access to his Fox-Davies Archive; generously allowing it to be removed for study and permission to reproduce a number of the illustrations in his possession.

Mrs Janet Whitehouse, for introducing me to the Fox-Davies and Helard material at Coalbrookdale and help with other biographical aspects.

Richard Downey, for providing me with the Downey correspondence and other information concerning the Helard plates engraved by his forebears.

Our President, James Wilson, whose holding of Helard plates he kindly allowed me to acquire. As a result I now have an almost complete collection of her known plates including size and colour variations which has made the task of writing very much easier.

My wife, Isobel, for her tolerance during the creation of this volume and for assisting with proof reading.

Damien Clements, for help with biographical information.

My grateful thanks go to fellow committee members Dr Geoffrey Vevers, Jim Shurmer and Peter Youatt for their expertise in scanning and refining all the illustrations and preparing the text for publication.

The following illustrations are reproduced by kind permission of Colonel Tony Molesworth:
Figs. 1 (frontispiece), 2, 4, 8, 9, 10, 12 and 18

Figs. 3a, 6 and 7 are reproduced by kind permission of Mrs Janet Whitehouse

The bookplate of Gwerfyl Barrett on page 111 is reproduced by kind permission of the National Library of Wales

Introduction

I was first alerted to the bookplates of Miss C. Helard (Mary Ellen Blanche Crookes) through my interest in heraldry. One day in 1978 I walked into a Cambridge antiquarian bookshop. The place was flooded out with books and quite clearly there had just been a large delivery. It turned out that the dealer had bought the entire library of the late Arthur Charles Fox-Davies (Helard's husband) the Edwardian lawyer, author and expert on heraldry.

As part of the purchase there were multiple copies of many of Fox-Davies's heraldic publications. Careful searching allowed me to locate and buy several volumes which had been personal copies of members of the family, identified either by bookplates or inscriptions. These included Helard's copy of 'The Book of Public Arms', which she co-authored with her future husband, signed 'Nellie Crookes June 1894' and Fox-Davies's copy of the fifth edition of 'Armorial Families' containing his bookplate by Graham Johnston as well as several other interesting volumes. It later transpired that the entire library, minus my few volumes, was sold 'en bloc' to a Japanese buyer.

Knowing my interest in bookplates the dealer told me that a quantity of ephemera including a large number of bookplates had been purchased from the same source by an Ipswich dealer. A visit to Ipswich produced even richer treasures. There were indeed many bookplates used by Fox-Davies in compiling his 'Armorial Families' and other publications. Unfortunately many were scribbled on and annotated and, therefore, useless as collectors' items. There were, however a number of original drawings, in good condition, mainly by Helard, John Forbes Nixon and Graham Johnston including his original drawing for Fox-Davies's own bookplate.

In addition, there was the real prize, a large brown envelope inscribed on the outside 'Bookplates of Miss C. Helard'. This contained over one-hundred and twenty different Helard plates mostly in mint condition. A few were showing slight signs of having been damp, with light foxing. I learnt, subsequently, that all the material, including the books, had been in store for many decades, since shortly after the death of Fox-Davies in 1928. They only came on the market following the death of his daughter, Mrs Moyra Regan, in 1972.

The Ipswich dealer also showed me a large, brown, leather bound album, gold stamped on the front 'Bookplates by C. Helard' containing twenty four of Helard's best plates which he did not wish to sell (see Appendix I). I did, however, buy the envelope of Helard plates and all the drawings plus a small quantity of correspondence. This archive, together with the books and further collecting, stimulated many years of interesting research culminating in this volume. The dealer also allowed me to borrow the leather bound album to check that there were no plates in it which were not included in the envelope – which proved to be the case. The album was returned and I do not know its present whereabouts.

Following my purchase our President, Jim Wilson, also made a call on the Ipswich dealer and bought a quantity of bookplates including some Helard plates which I had either missed or not been shown. They included a number which were not in the envelope or were of a different size or colour. I am grateful to Jim in that, when I started writing this book, he allowed me to acquire the whole of his Helard holdings on an exchange basis. This greatly assisted my researches.

Helard's story is inevitably tied up with that of her husband, Arthur Charles Fox-Davies, both before and after their marriage. Another huge help has been the discovery of two of the present members of the Fox-Davies family, Mrs Janet Whitehouse and Colonel Tony Molesworth. The former, granddaughter of A.C. Fox-Davies's younger brother George, introduced me to a lot of material in Coalbrookdale. The latter, whose late wife, Nicola, was Helard's granddaughter, holds a considerable Fox-Davies Archive including letters, family trees, photographs and other documents which he very generously allowed me to borrow and reproduce which has greatly enhanced the content of this book.

The quantity of Helard plates is small compared to the output of artists such as C.W. Sherborn and G.W. Eve, only somewhat over a hundred and thirty plates, excluding size and colour variations. However, she can certainly stand alongside these two Masters, in quality if not in quantity. (See fig. 15).

Despite years of search and research I would not claim that this is a complete record of all Helard's bookplate oeuvre. It is however, a record of all the plates known to me at the present time and I believe it to be fairly complete. Nevertheless I should be pleased to hear of any additional plates which may come to light subsequently.

It has not been possible to identify details of the owners of one or two of the plates and again I should be pleased to hear of any further information.

Finally, I have designed this book so that each section can stand alone. This has involved some slight repetition in places but, I believe makes for easier reading and reference.

Family Histories

The Crookes/Proctor Families

Mary Ellen Blanche Crookes (Miss C. Helard) was born on 7 October 1870 at 5 St Mary's Terrace East, Lexden Road Colchester in Essex. She was known as Nellie in the family and later as Nell by her husband. She was the eldest child of Septimus Wilkinson Crookes and his wife Annie, nee Proctor. At the time of her birth her father was a brewer in partnership as Daniell Bros and Crookes in Colchester.

Her forebears on both sides were respectable middle class folk. The Crookes were originally from Sheffield and connected with the iron industry. Septimus's father, Charles, was born there in 1805 as was his mother, Ann Robinson Wilkinson, in 1806. They were married in Sheffield around 1830 and then moved to Northampton where their first two children were born, Martha Ann in 1832 and Ellen in 1834. Later in the 1830s the family moved to Coalbrookdale, Shropshire where they had another four children, Maria, Charles, Fanny and the youngest, Septimus, born on 29 March 1844.

Charles's occupation is described on Septimus's birth certificate as 'modeller'. In 1851 he is described as 'Agent to an Iron Founder' and in 1861 as 'Iron Master'. In fact he was a designer and the manager of the famous Coalbrookdale Iron Company from 1850 to 1866 having worked for the company since the late 1830s. When he took over the management there was a workforce of over three thousand employees producing two thousand pounds weight of ironwork a week and it was, probably, the largest foundry in the world.

The company was originally owned by the Darby family, one of whose members, Abraham Darby III, built the first iron bridge in England, over the river Severn, at Ironbridge in 1779. This led the way to the second, much larger, iron bridge over the river Wear in Sunderland in 1796. It was following the retirement of the last Darby, Abraham IV, that Charles became manager. He and his family lived at Paradise House, an early 19th century house in Paradise on the edge of Ironbridge. The area was originally known as Paradise Fields, then Paradise Row and finally just Paradise.

Charles was a man of some stature and ability in the Coalbrookdale iron industry. He was the designer of the Coalbrookdale Literary and Scientific Institute built by The Coalbrookdale Company, just along the lane from his home, and opened in 1859. It was an attempt, by educating the workforce and their families, to improve the design and artistic quality of the company's products. He designed and exhibited a fine set of bronze gates at the Great Exhibition of 1851 which were later erected in Kensington Gardens, London, near the Albert Memorial. The company achieved more success at the 1862 Exhibition and in 1863 they began the production of locomotives. In the same year the Albert Edward Bridge carrying the railway over the river Severn was erected. Charles's cousin was the well known scientist and spiritualist Sir William Crookes OM, FRS inventor of, amongst other things, the Crookes Radiometer.

In the early 1860s tragedy struck the Crookes family. Their son, Charles Torkington died aged just twenty-two on 10 December 1862 followed by his mother Anne, aged fifty-seven, on 2 January 1863. Septimus's sisters Maria, aged twenty-seven, died in 1864 and Fanny, aged twenty-three, died in 1865. They are all buried in the family grave in Holy Trinity Churchyard in Coalbrookdale as is Nellie's father Septimus, who died in 1881. Following the decimation of his family Charles retired from the Coalbrookdale Company in 1866 and left the area. His later movements are not known.

Nellie's mother, Anne Blanche Harriet Proctor, came of a long line of physicians. Her father, grandfather and great grandfather were all doctors in the Shropshire area. Her father, Richard Fellowes Proctor, was a general practitioner in Ironbridge. With his wife, Mary, he had six children. Two of his sons John Ward and James became doctors. John Ward married Sarah Rose, the daughter of John Rose founder of the Coalport Porcelain Factory. One of his daughters, Mary, married Sir Charles Buckworth-Herne-Soame Bart. and another, Eliza, married a wealthy local farmer John Titterton. Most of these people we shall meet again as Nellie's life story unfolds.

Septimus Crookes and Anne Proctor were married in the Parish Church, Holy Trinity, in Coalbrookdale on 16 May 1867. Septimus had started his working life, with his father, as a clerk in the Coalbrookdale Ironworks. I have seen him referred to in print as 'Captain' Septimus Crookes and there is evidence that he served in a Volunteer Battalion. At some stage he moved into the brewing industry and became a brewer in partnership with the Daniell family in Colchester which is where he was living at the time of his marriage.

His other claim to fame seems to be that, whilst in Coalbrookdale, he taught Captain Matthew Webb, the well known Channel swimmer, to swim. Webb was a local man from Dawley who swam the English Channel, from Dover to Calais on 24 August 1875 and died attempting to swim the Niagara River on 24 July 1885.

The Daniell family had been brewers in Colchester from the 1850s under various titles, Daniell, Daniell and Sons, Daniell Bros and finally from the late 1860s Daniell Bros and Crookes. The business was at the Castle Brewery in Maidenburgh Street.

The Crookes's family home was at 5 St Mary's Terrace East, Lexden Road in Colchester, a fine late regency style house built in 1837. Here they lived in some comfort, following Nellie's birth, with a nurse, cook and housemaid. Over the next few years Nellie was joined by a sister, Lilian Ada, in 1874, a brother, Charles Philip, in 1876 and another sister, Gertrude Dorothy, in December 1877.

In 1878 a major fire destroyed the Castle Brewery and Septimus left the business. Shortly thereafter the couple, with their children, moved to Coalbrookdale to The Wyke, a family home near Shifnal, possibly to be nearer their families. Probably, at that time Septimus was showing signs of ill-health. A final child Cecil was born in October 1880.

On 27 March 1881, at the age of only thirty-six, Septimus died. He was attended by his brother-in-law, Dr John Ward Proctor, in his last illness and Dr Proctor signed the death certificate certifying that Septimus died of congestion of the lung of eleven days duration complicated by cirrhosis of the liver of five months duration. The commonest cause of cirrhosis of the liver in those days was excessive alcohol consumption no doubt an occupational hazard in the brewing industry.

His will was signed only fourteen days before he died and was witnessed by his wife's brother-in-law, Charles Buckworth-Herne-Soame, surgeon (later to inherit his uncle's baronetcy as the 9th baronet) and his wife's sister Eliza Titterton. He left '*all my household furniture, plate, linen, china and other household effects and the sum of one hundred pounds*' to his wife for her sole use. The rest of his estate both real and personal he left in trust to be converted into cash and the proceeds invested in government stocks in England, Wales or India, or in any railway company in England and Wales. This was a standard formulation for wills at that time used by many testators. Investments in the railways and the Empire were deemed to be sound. The dividends were to be paid to his wife for her sole use and, after her death, the capital was to pass to his sons and daughters in equal shares.

The value of his estate was given as under £5,000, a sum equivalent to about £400,000 in today's terms. We do not know the exact amount of the legacy but if we assume it to be £4,000, that invested at 3.5%, the going rate at that time, would bring in £140 per annum, or about £2-13s-od (£2.65p) per week. It seems a very small amount of money by today's values but one must remember that a labourer's wage at that time was less than a £1 a week on which to support a family, so the Crookes family could and did survive on that income or even a lesser sum.

Four days after Septimus's death the Census Return, on 31 March 1881, shows the family split up temporarily (probably between the death and the funeral) but in the same area. Mother remains at home with her sister Eliza Titterton, a nurse and two servants, whilst her two doctor brothers come to the rescue of the children. Nellie, Lilian and Charles are staying with Dr James Proctor at Severn Cottage in Ironbridge, where they are described as visitors. Gertrude and the baby, Cecil, are staying with Dr John Ward Proctor at Idsall House, Shifnal. As well as being a physician he was also a farmer, in a small way, with eighty-four acres, employing four farm labourers.

The family seemed to have a little difficulty deciding on Cecil's name. He was registered, on 10 December 1880 as Cecil Reginald but on the Census Return in March 1881 the enumerator first put down 'Ben', crossed it out and wrote 'Reginald E.'.

At some time in the 1880s Mrs Crookes and her family moved to Castletown on the Isle of Man where, with the exception of Nellie, they can be found in 1891 living at Rose Cottage 28 Bowling Green Road with one general domestic servant. Nellie's whereabouts at that time has not been ascertained despite a careful search of the Census Returns.

She was certainly visiting London in the early 1890s; a silhouette of her taken in 1893 shows her as a very fashionable young lady of her time. It is inscribed on the back 'MEBC, Earls Court Exhibition, July 13th 1893' (see fig. 2).

The next time she can be located is in July 1896 when she was elected a member of the Ex Libris Society under her newly acquired pseudonym of 'C. Helard' (see Section III) and her address is given as Cromwell House, Huntingdon, sixty miles north of London. She remained a member of the Ex Libris Society until 1905.

Cromwell House is a large, detached dwelling standing in its own grounds in the High Street and rebuilt, in 1810, on the site of an earlier house in which Oliver Cromwell was born. It was bought in 1876 by Isaac Bernard and his wife Mary. They lived there with their son William and a staff of four servants. He was a retired sea captain who had worked for the Peninsular and Oriental Steam Navigation Company. There is some suggestion that the family were related to the Fox-Davieses and therefore Helard might have known them. Isaac died in 1894 but his wife stayed on in the house until 1912. It is possible that Helard went as a companion to the new widow. During the time she was there she produced a bookplate for the son William Cecil Bernard (H005). Even in those days Huntingdon was little

Fig. 2
Silhouette of Nellie Crookes taken at The Earls Court Exhibition and inscribed on the reverse 'M.E.B.C. Earls Court Exhibition, 13 July 1893'

over an hour by train to London where her future husband, Charles Fox-Davies, lived and worked so it would have been a convenient place to live, possibly rent free. She was living there for at least three years before moving, in 1899, to be with her family in Rose Cottage on the Isle of Man.

Thereafter the whole family moved back to Shropshire where in March 1901 they are living in The White Cottage, Paradise, Ironbridge. Nellie is described as *'an heraldic artist living on her own means'* and her mother is described as a lady *'of independent means'*. Her brother, Charles, is still living at home and is a mechanical engineer probably working for the Coalbrookdale Company. He later moved to Bath.

A month later Nellie married Arthur Charles Fox-Davies, a local boy, whom she had known since her teens and with whom she had been collaborating over various heraldic publications. There had obviously been a developing relationship over many years some of the time being spent apart, he in London and she in various parts of the country.

That she missed him is in no doubt and borne out by a poem she wrote sometime in the early 1890s and which is, almost certainly, dedicated to Charlie. It was found, written and signed, on the back page of an exercise book which was full of cooking recipes, in Nell's handwriting, and titled *'Mammon's Victim by M.E.B.C., dedicated to My Mother'* It looks as though the book was intended for publication but there is no evidence that it ever happened:

> *'Oh Promise Me.'*
> *'Oh promise me that some day you and I*
> *Shall meet and never part until we die*
> *Oh promise me that though I have you here*
> *In time to come I shall not be less dear*
> *For months and years will but increase my love*
> *And absence wheresoever I may move*
> *Will link my heart with closer chains to thee*
> *Oh promise me Oh promise me*
> *Oh promise me that none shall take my place*
> *That none shall look in love upon your face*
> *Let me though all unworthy such a prize*
> *Read now your love for me in your dear eyes*
> *For then can I with courage leave you now*
> *Leaving with fullest heart your given vow*
> *There, Love if you will have me happy be*
> *Oh promise me Oh promise me.'*
>
> *Nellie Crookes*

Fig. 3a
Architect's impression of The Villa, Coalbrookdale c.1865. Built by John Fox JP and occupied by the family until the late 1960s

Fig. 3b
The Villa, Coalbrookdale as it appears today. It is now a Guest House

They married in 1901. It may have been a lack of financial security that delayed their marriage. Both of them suffered from irregular and uncertain income. The age of thirty was very late to get married, in those days, when they had known each other since their teens.

Later in the decade Nellie's mother, Annie, moved down to Batheaston, near Bath, to live with her son Charles. She died there in March 1911.

The Davies/Fox/Fox-Davies Families

The Davies family, in the paternal line, are of Welsh descent. Thomas Davies, son of David Davies of Carmarthen was baptised there in 1770. He married Jane Edmonds of Carmarthen in 1792 and they had eight sons and six daughters. At least ten of them survived into adulthood. In his will, dated 1822 Thomas left £150 to each of his five younger children when they came of age. He had already provided £150 to each of his five older children; all this in spite of the fact that he was illiterate and could only sign his will with an 'X'. He died in 1827.

Charles, the youngest son, lived most of his life in Cardigan where he was an ironmonger and where, in January 1839, he married Mary Herring, daughter of the local Baptist Minister, the Reverend John Herring, a man of some standing in his community. Their son, Thomas Edmond Davies was born in Cardigan on 20 November 1839 at. '*40 minutes past 9 o'clock in the evening*'. He was the eldest of eight children.

In 1868 Thomas was living in Bristol, working, as an agent of the Coalbrookdale Iron Company. In the same year he married Maria Jane Fox, in Holy Trinity Church, Coalbrookdale. Maria was the elder daughter and co-heiress of John Fox JP of Coalbrookdale, alderman, accountant and one time Mayor of Wenlock, and his wife Hannah, daughter of George Goodwin of Ironbridge.

John Fox was a leading figure in the Coalbrookdale Iron Company and, in the 1860s, built himself a substantial family home, The Villa, in Paradise a lane running parallel to the Dale Road down into Ironbridge. The postal address was simply 'The Villa, Coalbrookdale, Shropshire.' So it was obviously a house of some standing and importance. It was designed on four floors (see fig. 3a) with domestic facilities and servants quarters on the ground and top floors and the family rooms on the middle two floors with steps up to the first floor. At some stage either during building or later a small two storey staff wing was added on the left hand side. It was to be the family's home for over one-hundred years, until the 1960s. Today it is run as a guest house (see fig. 3b).

After their marriage Thomas and Maria lived in Bristol for some years at 5 Springfield Road and by 1871 they had a family of two sons John Fox born in 1869 and Arthur Charles born in 1871.

Within the year Thomas was transferred to the head office in Coalbrookdale and the family moved to Severn Cottage, Ironbridge and increased by a further three children, George Edward born in 1874, Grace Muriel born in 1876 and Irene Isabelle born in 1878 (see fig. 4). Later they moved to Paradise House, an early 19th century house two doors down from The Villa in Paradise and previously occupied by Charles Crookes.

It would appear that Thomas had ambitions to improve his status in life, almost certainly, urged on by his second son, Charlie and possibly by his father-in-law. On 28 February 1890 (his nineteenth birthday) Charlie changed his name by Deed Poll adding Fox before Davies to his surname. In 1894, his father, Thomas, received a Royal Licence, signed by the Queen, authorising him and his issue by his wife Maria Jane to assume the surname of Fox in addition to and before that of Davies. His father-in-law, John Fox, had died the previous year. Thomas

Fig. 4
Mr and Mrs Thomas Edmond Fox-Davies and family *c.*1885.
(*Back row left to right*) John (Jack), Thomas Edmond, Charlie.
(*Front row left to right*) Grace, George, Irene and Maria Jane

was granted arms in 1905 with limitation to him and his descendants and to the other descendants of his late father Charles Davies. The application was made by his son Charlie (see Appendix II). The family were on their way to joining the Establishment.

By 1891 the two elder boys had left home. Charlie was in London lodging with Charles Maltby, a bank manager and his wife, at 156 Railton Road Brixton, occupying two rooms and describing himself as an editor and author, leaving George at home working as a bank clerk. The three brothers were eventually reunited in London where, in 1901, they were sharing lodgings in a boarding house at 173 Kings Road, St Pancras. The owner was a widowed lady, Mrs Mary Barnes. John (Jack) was an engineer manager, Charlie an editor, author and journalist and George was still a bank clerk working for Lloyds Bank. Charlie was about to be married.

Thomas Edmond Fox-Davies died during an influenza epidemic on 23 January 1908. He left an estate valued at just under £1,500 to his wife, Maria. She had already inherited The Villa under the will of her late father and following the death of her mother in 1899 the family had moved there. After Thomas's death Maria lived on in The Villa with her two unmarried daughters, Grace and Irene, until her death at the age of eighty-nine in 1937. The two sisters remained in the family home until their deaths in the 1960s and Miss Grace and Miss Irene are remembered in Coalbrookdale to this day.

Thomas had earlier left instructions concerning the disposal of his body after death.

'I consider the proper way to dispose of the dead is by cremation but as this apparently does not meet with approval on my wife's part and as she may have a desire to be buried with me, I direct her to dispose of my remains as she will and deposit them where she pleases provided that the strictest economy consistent with safety and decency be observed. I do not believe in robbing the living to gratify Mrs Grundy's idea of what should be wished upon the dead for the benefit of undertakers and other strangers. I desire only to live in the memories and affections of those who love me.'

He is buried in Holy Trinity Churchyard in Coalbrookdale in a substantial family grave along with his wife and other members of his family. The Church of The Holy Trinity was built at the behest and expense of the last of the Darby family, Abraham IV and his brother and sisters. It was consecrated in 1854. (See fig. 5). The churchyard contains the graves of the majority of the Crookes,

Fig. 5 Holy Trinity Church, Coalbrookdale. The cross half way down on the right hand side , in line with the church door marks the grave of Charles Fox-Davies and his wife, Miss C. Helard

Fox and Fox-Davies families for the last one-hundred and fifty years and there are detailed memorials to these families inside the church which has also seen most of their weddings and christenings.

The Fox-Davies / Crookes Family

Charlie Fox-Davies and Nell Crookes were married on Tuesday 30 April 1901 at Holy Trinity Church, Coalbrookdale. In the absence of her father the bride was given away by her uncle Dr John Ward Proctor. Her bridesmaids were her sisters Lilian and Gertrude and Charlie's sisters Grace and Irene There were a large number of

Fig. 6
The Wedding Party,
30 April 1901.
Extreme left brother
John (best man) and
wife Caroline (hat),
then brother George
and wife Eva, then two
of the bridesmaids,
Nell's sisters Gertrude
and Lilian. The
groom, Charlie, is in
the centre standing
back. On the right
Charlie's parents
Thomas and Maria
Fox-Davies and his
sisters, Grace and
Irene (bridesmaids)

guests including the Countess of Yarborough, Sir Charles
Buckworth-Herne-Soame Bart., Dr John Ward Proctor, Mr
Carlyon-Britton and Admiral Pollard, all of whom feature
in the bookplate list.

Fig. 6 shows the Wedding Party before the ceremony. I
say 'before' because, quite clearly, the bride is missing.
The photograph is probably taken either at The Villa or in
the churchyard. On the far left are Charlie's elder brother
John (best man) and his wife Caroline; next is his younger
brother George and his wife Eva and then Nellie's sisters,
Lilian and Gertrude (bridesmaids). In the middle and set
back is the bridegroom, Charlie. In the right foreground are
his parents Thomas and Maria and his sisters, Grace and
Irene (bridesmaids). The bride is elsewhere presumably
leaving her home or her uncle's house for the ceremony.
However, by good fortune, a photograph of the bride,
in her wedding dress, has been discovered. For those
interested and who understand such matters I can reveal
that, according to the newspaper report she wore *'a dress of
white glace silk covered with a transparent white silk grenadine, with
lace flounces and pearl embroidery, and a handsome veil of old Mechlin
lace,'* (see fig. 7). The groom presented each bridesmaid with
a gold signet ring.

After a reception at the White House hosted by the
bride's mother and a honeymoon in the Channel Islands the
couple set up home in London living at various addresses in
the early part of their married life. Their first home was at

(*Right*) Fig. 7 The bride, Nell, in her wedding finery

34 Hogarth Road, South Kensington where Nell held her first formal 'At Home' on 6, 7 and 8 June for which she issued printed cards.

Like the good lawyer he was to become Charlie acknowledged his new marital status by writing his will which is still in the Fox-Davies Archive. It was short and to the point. *'I give devise and bequeath all of which I may die possessed to my wife, Mary Ellen Blanche Fox-Davies formerly Crookes whom I appoint Executrix'*. The last phrase *'whom I appoint Executrix'* is in a different ink and a different hand. It appears to have been added later. The will was witnessed by his father and his brother Jack and dated 5 August 1901. His father, Thomas, made an identical will two months later leaving everything to his wife, Maria.

Charlie and Nell both led extremely busy lives (see Sections II and III) but still found time to raise a family. Their daughter was born on 17 October 1903 at 132 Cromwell Road, London W. When her birth was registered five weeks later on 28 November they had still not found a name for her. She was subsequently given the names Moyra de Somery. She was baptised on 14 March 1904, not in London but in Holy Trinity Church, Coalbrookdale. Amongst others her godparents were, the Countess of Yarborough and Helard's sister Lilian.

Fig. 8
The Fox-Davies family *c.*1910.
In the front are Nell and the children, Harley and Moyra, *and at the back*, Charlie and his sister Grace.
Taken at The Villa, Coalbrookdale

Fig. 9
The Fox-Davies family
c.1920.
In the front Harley,
seated Moyra, Nell and her
sister, Lilian,
standing Charlie

Four years later her brother was born on 17 September 1907 at 15 Stratford Road, London W. He was named Harley Edmond Fitzroy. He was baptised the following month at St Philip's Church, Kensington. Two of his godparents were Sir John Mark and his uncle, George Edward Fox-Davies. By that time his father had become a barrister having been called to the bar as a member of Lincoln's Inn in 1906.

In 1911 the family were still living at 15 Stratford Road. Nell's two sisters, Lilian and Gertrude were staying with them and described as 'ladies of independent means'. The establishment was supported by two servants, Amy Watson a nursery governess and Charlotte Wellard a general domestic servant (see fig. 8).

Sometime after that the family moved to another rented property, 65 Warwick Gardens, West Kensington where the parents remained for the rest of their married life. Charlie had Chambers at 23 Old Buildings, Lincoln's Inn. Although he had a career as a barrister, his fame, today, rests on his heraldic writings and, to a lesser extent on his crime fiction (see Section II).

Nell, as well as designing bookplates as C. Helard, also wrote stories and serials using her mother's maiden name as 'Mary Proctor'. A play in three Acts entitled 'Chance' under the name of Mary Fox-Davies was produced by The Kensington Amateur Dramatic Club in 1927, running for two nights, 8 and 9 November at The Rudolf Steiner Theatre in Baker Street. Nell's daughter, Moyra, played one of the lead parts. It is not clear, from the family archives, whether the playwright was Nell or, less likely, her niece, Mary, daughter of Charlie's elder brother John.

Their son, Harley, was educated at Radley and went on to the Royal Military College at Sandhurst where he was a Prize Cadet. He joined the 2nd Battalion Durham Light Infantry and saw service in India in the 1920s and 30s. During the Second World War he served in Egypt with the 1st Battalion Durham Light Infantry, where he achieved the rank of major, and was co-opted into the Long Range Desert Group. He was awarded the Military Cross, but sadly, was killed in action, near Fort Cappuzzio in the Libyan Desert, on 15 May 1941. He is buried in the Halfaya Sollum War Cemetery in Egypt.

Their daughter, Moyra, remained at home until she married, at the age of thirty, in 1934. She married Robert Sanders Regan whose father was a sheep farmer. Robert was a hospital secretary and a Lieutenant in the RNVR. They had one daughter, Nicola, born 15 May 1941. She was registered as 'Nicola Moyra Sarah' but this was changed, after registration, to 'Nicola Harley Sarah' no doubt in memory of her uncle who had been killed on the day that she was born. She grew up to marry Colonel Tony Molesworth, who currently holds the Fox-Davies Archive. Her mother, Moyra (see fig. 9), died on 10 January 1972 at The Gordon Hospital, Westminster.

Charles Fox-Davies died on 9 May 1928. *The Times* obituary, on 21 May said,

'Mr Arthur Charles Fox-Davies, genealogist, barrister and author, died on Saturday at the age of 57 at his home in Warwick Gardens, where he had been lying ill for some weeks.'

In fact he died in Guy's Hospital in a coma. He had been suffering from portal hypertension and cirrhosis of the liver. A condition, like that of his late father-in-law, most likely brought on by over indulgence in alcohol. He is buried in the churchyard at Coalbrookdale.

Nell continued to produce the occasional bookplate after his death, mostly from half tone blocks. Her last known, dated, plate being in 1932 but these plates are nowhere near the quality of her earlier work.

Between 1928 and 1930 she was also writing articles for an Australian newspaper, *The Brisbane Courier*, at two guineas a time. The arrangement was terminated by the editor in May 1930 because, as he said, *'of a rearrangement of our news services'*.

She remained in the family home, 65 Warwick Gardens, until early in 1934 by which time her health was deteriorating. She then went to live next door to her son at 181 Cromwell Road.

She died, intestate, on 25 April 1935 at the Princess Beatrice Hospital, London, where she had been suffering from post-operative pneumonia having undergone major surgery for cancer of the bladder. Letters of Administration were granted to her daughter, Mrs Moyra Regan. She left a personal estate valued at £530-1s-0d.

She was cremated and her ashes were interred in her husband's grave in Holy Trinity Churchyard, Coalbrookdale on 30 April 1935. (see fig. 5).

On 28 February 1954 the anniversary of Charlie's birthday, an illuminated armorial stone plaque was unveiled in the church by the family, the inscription reads:

AD MAJOREM DEI GLORIAM
ET IN MEMORIAM
ARTHUR CHARLES FOX-DAVIES
GENTLEMAN OF LINCOLN'S INN, BARRISTER
AT LAW,
A LIFE LONG STUDENT OF HERALDRY,
AUTHOR OF NUMEROUS WORKS
AND AN ACKNOWLEDGED AUTHORITY ON
THAT SUBJECT,
HE WAS BORN FEBRUARY 28TH 1871 THE
SECOND SON OF

THOMAS EDMOND FOX-DAVIES, GENTLEMAN
OF COALBROOKDALE,
AND MARIA JANE HIS WIFE. HE DIED
MAY 19TH 1928
IN MEMORY ALSO OF
MARY ELLEN BLANCHE, HIS WIFE,
FIRST DAUGHTER OF SEPTIMUS WILKINSON
CROOKES ESQUIRE
OF THE WYKE, SHIFNAL
SHE WAS BORN OCTOBER 7TH 1870 AND DIED
APRIL 25TH 1935
ALSO OF THEIR ONLY SON
HARLEY EDMOND FOX-DAVIES ESQ. M.C.
MAJOR THE DURHAM LIGHT INFANTRY
BORN SEPTEMBER 17TH 1907 KILLED IN
ACTION NEAR
FORT CAPPUZZIO IN THE LIBYAN DESERT
MAY 15TH 1941

It is noticeable that whilst there is detailed and fulsome information given concerning Charlie and his son, there is little concerning Nell's achievements.

Amongst the family papers is a poem commemorating the occasion, dated 28 February 1954 composed most probably by their daughter Moyra.

Da Fydd
To A.C.F-D.

Today, in the gentle Church upon the hill
The stone was set.
Your name, your arms
That proud coat you bore for shield,
Its colours glow, deep and limpid in the calm light,
A golden sun upon a sable field.
Your crest and badge of gules.
Dear one, was this indeed the sum of all you gave me?
Your sword now sheathed,
Your armour layed aside.
The fight is ended and the long trail done.
And here in the place where your fathers bide
Sleep comes, and peace at eventide.

Coalbrookdale 28. 2. 54.

It is clear from reviewing the family papers that the four families, Crookes, Proctor, Davies and Fox, over the generations, lived in a close knit community in Ironbridge, Coalbrookdale. They were on visiting terms with each other and even, at different times, lived in the same houses. When they first came to Ironbridge from Bristol Thomas Davies and family lived in Severn Cottage in the 1870s and Dr James Proctor and family lived there in the 1880s. Thomas and his family then moved to Paradise House which had previously been the home of Helard's grandfather Charles Crookes when he was manager for the Coalbrookdale Company. Finally Thomas and his family moved to The Villa following the death of his mother-in-law Hannah Fox in 1899.

We have been left an account of the village of Coalbrookdale written by Charlie's sister Grace Fox-Davies, in the 1950s:

'My Village is Coalbrookdale, a lovely winding valley that runs between wooded hillsides down to a beautiful stretch of the Severn Valley Gorge. These wooded slopes are broken up on the left as we descend, by fields, dwellings with gardens and other buildings and high up among them stands a modern but most pleasing stone Church. On the right, along the upper part of the valley are the Iron Works to which, in the past, Coalbrookdale owed its fame, for they produced extremely fine iron and bronze castings. These were cast in moulds of local sand and were unrivalled for delicacy and finish. Other Works, in various parts of the country, have now ousted us from our position of priority and artistic castings are no longer made here.

We are still proud of the fact that the first iron bridge was made at Coalbrookdale and a very handsome pair of Coalbrookdale gates guard one entrance to Hyde Park. (London) Moreover, we claim the first iron boat, the idea of which occurred to Mr. John Wilkinson when, after a high flood, he saw some of the Coalbrookdale Company's three-legged iron pots floating down the river.

It is surprising how little the Work's buildings detract from the beauty of the valley and from certain points of view they are almost or quite invisible. In no case, however, do we grumble about them. They have meant a living to us, or to our forebears and we should not be here without them.

The village of Coalbrookdale is very old. It dates back to at least as far as the thirteenth century and may be older still. It was originally, I suppose, an agricultural village but is really an industrial centre in a rural setting. Farms and fields still enclose it. As we go down the valley or, to use the local expression, 'down the dale', the woods on the right are less broken up till they reach the main road at the bottom of the valley. Here there are houses and a fine modern school. The railway, which terminates the tree belt, is not a blot on the landscape and the station is decidedly pretty.

This is a quiet place when our grand peal of ten bells are not ringing and we are a quiet people though most of us, urged by conscience or circumstances, are genuinely busy. We are rather incurious, we work quietly and modestly, and are often half ignorant of each other's meritorious activities.'

Arthur Charles Fox-Davies 1871–1928

Arthur Charles Fox-Davies was born in Bristol on 28 February 1871. He was raised in Coalbrookdale, Shropshire and educated at Ackworth, a Quaker school founded in 1779 near Pontefract in Yorkshire, before spending his working life in London. He was known in the family as Charlie. He has left behind a vivid account of his early life which I found in the Fox-Davies Archive.

Of his time at Ackworth he says: '*Of the School itself and the life there various books have been written. As for myself, I hated and loathed the place from the time I went to the time I left. I have scarcely any pleasant recollections of it and I had not a solitary regret in leaving it*'.

With his father's permission he left at Christmas 1885, at the age of fourteen, following a 'difference of opinion' with the teaching staff. He had actually struck a master.

His father gave him the choice of going on to King Edward's School in Birmingham or going to work. He chose to go to work. Through the good offices of a friend and colleague of his father's, Mr W.G. Norris, he was offered a post at the Coalbrookdale Iron Works as a junior clerk in his Department, at an initial wage of £20 a year. William Gregory Norris had followed Charles Crookes as manager of the Coalbrookdale Company Ltd. from 1866 until 1890.

In the first half of 1887 (Golden Jubilee Year) Charlie kept a diary. The entries, on the whole, were short, to the point and not very interesting apart from the rather startling entry on 4 April, '*Fred Bailey cut his throat,*' no further information is forthcoming. On the 28 February, his sixteenth birthday, he records his presents, '*Father, razor and strop, Mother, 2/6d, Aunt Hannah, 2/6d, Jack* (older brother), *card case, George* (younger brother*), drawing book and chalks.*' He seems to have spent his time in the summer of 1887 either rowing on the river Severn or having tea and going for walks with various young ladies.

Perhaps the most interesting entries from our point of view occur over the last weekend in April. Friday 22 '*Bachelor Ball*' in large bold letters; Saturday 23 '*Walk with Miss Nellie Crookes*', Sunday 24 '*Same with Nellie Crookes*'. Was this the beginning of the life-long relationship? The other

entry of note was 24 March, '*Mr Norris lent me Berry's Heraldry'*. His interest in the subject was already aroused. Some years later in his *Introduction to The Book of Public Arms*, 1894 he refers his readers for general information on heraldry to one of the recognised handbooks on the subject saying '*Berry is my favourite*'.

Although gaining some preferment at the Coalbrookdale Works, his salary rising to £80 a year, he again fell out with his colleagues and left in April 1890 following the retirement of his boss W.G. Norris and a reorganisation of the office. During his time with the Coalbrookdale Company he was a keen member of their Rowing Club and Honorary Secretary of the Literary and Scientific Institute.

After a few months of idleness at home he secured a position with Messrs T.C. & E.C. Jack Publishers, of The Grange Publishing Works, Edinburgh, in their London office. His task was to edit and bring out a revised edition of *Fairbairn's Crests* at a salary of £150 a year. As he records, '*My previous publications had been 'A Flora of Ackworth and District' which I published whilst at School and 'the Salop Annual' which I wrote for a Shrewsbury printer* [Fred W. Jervis – published Christmas 1890] *and never got paid for.*' Thus began a writing career as an editor and journalist and the publication of his many heraldic works.

As a bachelor in London he lodged for some months with Mrs Mathew Webb the widow of the channel swimmer. He had previously met Matthew Webb the Sunday after his famous channel swim when he was visiting Coalbrookdale (see Appendix III).

He studied law. He was admitted a member of Lincoln's Inn in 1901 and was called to the Utter Bar on Gaudy Night in 1906 by the famous advocate Sir Edward Clark, then Treasurer of Lincoln's Inn. The event was reported in *The Cardigan and Tivy-Side Advertiser*, Friday 26 January 1906 in typical parochial fashion:

LEGAL EXAMINATIONS, – Amongst those who are announced as having passed the recent Bar Examinations with honours is Mr Arthur Charles Fox-Davies, whose name is 'screened' to be called in Lincoln's Inn on the 26th inst. He is the second son of

Mr T.E. Fox-Davies of Coulbrookdale (sic)*, and is at present editor of Dod's Peerage and Armorial Families. His grandmother was Mrs Charles Davies, the wife of Charles Davies of the firm of Lloyd, Davies and Myers, ironmongers, Cardigan Mrs Davies being the daughter of Mr John Herring, Baptist Minister, of Cardigan.*

In a letter to his mother thanking his parents for their congratulations it is clear he had been having financial difficulties and has to ask for the loan of his fees, £101-17-0, which had to be paid before he could be called to the Bar. He promises to pay it back, as he has done other loans in the past.

He practised on the South Eastern Circuit, at the Old Bailey and at the Surrey and South London Sessions (see fig. 10). He had a successful career at the Bar including presenting a number of Peerage Claim Cases to the House of Lords.

During the Coronation of King George V in 1911 he served as a Gold Staff Officer to the Earl Marshal, one of two-hundred and fifty Gold Staff Officers who assisted the Earl Marshal in preparing and conducting the ceremony. This post is not to be confused with that of Gold Stick in Waiting of whom there are only two and only one on duty at any one time attending the Sovereign on State Occasions. In England that office is held jointly by the Colonels of The Life Guards and The Blues and Royals.

Fig. 10
Arthur Charles
Fox-Davies,
Barrister-at-
Law, *c.*1918

Although he had a good working relationship with many members of the College of Arms, Fox-Davies never became a Pursuivant nor a Herald.

He took an active interest in politics but with remarkably little success. He stood for election under the Conservative banner as MP for Merthyr Tydfil in 1910, 1923 and 1924, without once achieving election; not surprising in Merthyr Tydfil. He was, however, elected as a member of Holborn Borough Council in London. He was enrolled as a Knight Imperial of the Primrose League in June 1898. This was an organisation for spreading Conservative principles in Great Britain. It was founded in 1883 and was active until the mid 1990s, being finally wound up in 2004.

During the First World War he served in the Anti-Aircraft Corp 1914–16, and in the naval law branch of the Admiralty 1916–20.

In addition to his serious writings he also wrote a number of works of crime fiction which are not easy to obtain today. They are typical of their period and draw heavily on his experience in the criminal courts. They were also published in America. Very few booksellers today are aware of his crime fiction although most are familiar with his heraldic writings.

His life's work, and real interest, was in the field of heraldry. As well as editing *Dod's Peerage*, *Burke's Landed Gentry*, *Fairbairn's Crests and Mottoes* he also edited the *Genealogical Magazine* from 1895–1906. This latter work was used frequently as a vehicle for expressing his opinions and 'puffing up' his other works and, also, drawing attention to his wife's bookplates and illustrations. His magnum opus, however, was *Armorial Families*, the first edition of which appeared in 1895 and the seventh, last, edition in two volumes in 1929 and 1930, after his death. His stated aim was to list every family in Britain who was legally entitled to bear arms, with the accent on the legally. He abhorred the bogus use of arms and what he called 'Stationer's Heraldry'. He ranted against them at every opportunity in his various publications.

He said, in an advertisement in the *Genealogical Magazine*, that the illustrations in the first edition of *Armorial Families* were by George Eve but in fact forty-eight of the one-hundred and twelve illustrations were by M.E.B. Crookes, the remainder, largely by George Eve and a few by John Forbes Nixon. All three were to feature largely in illustrating future Fox-Davies publications as was Graham Johnston, the herald painter to Lyon's Court in Edinburgh.

The illustrations in the first edition were placed at the

end of the volume usually five or nine to a page. In November/December 1893 Nellie Crookes was being paid fourteen shillings (70p) for a page of nine shields, but by February 1894 the price had gone up to £1 per page.

The sub-title to the first edition was '*A complete Peerage, Baronetage and Knightage and a Directory of some Gentlemen of Coat-Armour being the first attempt to show which arms in use at the moment are borne by Legal Authority*'. And therein lay Fox-Davies's main aim in life.

So many people tried to con him into accepting that they had a lawful right to the arms they were displaying, when this was not so, that he wrote –

'*Small wonder that with such a plenitude of these falsehoods my credulity waned below zero and is now non-existent.*'

There was a critique in the *Ex Libris Journal*, by W.H.K. Wright, written at the time of publication. Whilst, on the whole, commending the work he went on to say:

'*In a work of such a stupendous nature it would be absurd to expect complete accuracy at the outset. There are, however, many glaring mistakes in describing people as non-armigerous who are beyond doubt entitled to arms. We presume that the Author did not obtain the information from the persons themselves for they would scarcely describe themselves as non-armigerous and it therefore behoved him to make due enquiry before committing himself to a statement that such and such persons were 'ignobiles' for that is what it amounts to.*'

What proof, if any, the writer had for stating '*are beyond doubt entitled to arms*' I do not know but I suspect from what I have read that, on the whole, Fox-Davies's version was nearer the truth.

In 1898, as editor of the *Genealogical Magazine*, he was taken to task by a correspondent for declaring someone's arms as '*without lawful authority*'. A Mr Charles Kaines Smith wrote:

'*Now I take it that to condemn any coat of arms as not genuine when full particulars are not forthcoming is, to say the least of it, rash; and in this case more so as the coat can easily be proved to be genuine unless, indeed, a grant under the hand and seal of Robert Cooke, Clarenceux dated 1590 fails to satisfy the notoriously exacting Mr Fox-Davies.*'

In reply Fox-Davies says – '*the notoriously exacting Mr Fox-Davies (better be that than notoriously credulous) begs to admit his mistake.*'

Fox-Davies is not without a sense of humour. On another occasion he reported an event in the *Genealogical Magazine* (vol. II, p. 568) as follows:

'*At the Investiture of Lord Lucan as a Knight of St. Patrick, the Usher, Lord Charlemont, went to the wrong door to fetch the new knight and consequently there was some delay whilst he was 'lucan' for his lordship.*'

Following the first edition of *Armorial Families* there was much fluttering in the armorial family dovecotes as families hastened to put their heraldic houses in order. Some offered in support of their claim the statement that '*our family have used the arms from time immemorial*' but this cut no ice with Fox-Davies without documentary proof of some sort from the College of Arms, Lyon's Court or Ulster's Office.

By the third edition (1899) the publication was getting extremely bulky and it was decided, with one or two exceptions, to omit Peers and Baronets as they were adequately catered for in other publications such as *Burke's Peerage*.

Because of his strict attitude to proof he was taken to task by many critics particularly those who could not produce the necessary evidence. In reply he made a staunch defence against these attacks. In the preface to the fourth edition (1902) he says:

'*But it is to the general standpoint from which I write and on which I have compiled this book that my critics have chiefly devoted their attention. In all the reviews and criticisms of my work which I have read I have never come across anything which has disproved any of the broad lines which I have upheld in my heraldic writings. If my knowledge of the qualifications of the legal arms is wrong – it happens however, to be right – if, I say, it is wrong, I am open to be convinced.... But – and I especially commend this point to my critics – abuse does not prove that I am wrong, nor does point blank contradiction; nor would my standpoint be assailed successfully even if it could be proved that every pedigree contained in the Official Records happened to be a 'faked' one. Whilst the College of Arms in England remains the official authority it is useless to ask one's submissions elsewhere. If the public is dissatisfied with officialism it should urge reform, not vainly waste its strength and vituperative adjectives in the useless effort to prove that such official authority does not exist when it demonstrably does.*'

In 1870 Parliament had introduced a tax on the use and display of arms. For one guinea a year you could use and display arms except upon your carriage. For two guineas your carriage was included. The wording on the two guinea certificate read –

'*A— B— is hereby authorised to wear and use armorial bearings and to have the same painted, marked or affixed to any carriage.*'

This wording was like a red rag to a bull to Fox-Davies. He pointed out to the authorities that the wording, as it stood was 'ultra vires' and a direct infringement of the prerogative of the Sovereign. He suggests, *'with all possible deference'* to the authorities, that the following is more legal and less open to abuse:

'A— B— having paid the sum of two guineas, is hereby admitted to have fulfilled the requirements of the Inland Revenue Department, but such payment not to be held to have confirmed or conferred any right to the usage of arms not sanctioned by the duly accredited Officers of Arms.'

There was no response from the authorities. The tax brought in around £70,000 a year which is a measure of the number of people using armorial bearings at that time, whether legally or illegally, many more than *'the top ten thousand'* and it was not discontinued until 1944.

There is no doubt that as a result of the successive editions of *Armorial Families* over more than a quarter of a century a large number of families regularised their armorial displays. Initially, for those families who persisted in pleading their cause without documentary proof, Fox-Davies offered to print their entries in italics indicating no proven right to the arms. Some families agreed to this but by the fifth edition (1905) the practice was discontinued and unless proof could be given the entry was not included.

Nevertheless he notes in the preface to the fifth edition that he had written personally to the head of every family in *Burke's Landed Gentry* where he had no proof of their right to the arms they claimed asking if he might be advised if he were wrong. He goes on:

'The result of my letters astonished me. A very large number at once informed me of their right under a comparatively modern grant or record not to the ancient arms attributed to them but to some entirely distinct coat.'

By this time he is claiming that his *Armorial Families* is an almost complete record of those families, in Britain, legally entitled to bear arms. As a result, I think it would be fair to say that, following the publication of the final, seventh edition, any pre-1928 coat of arms not in one or other edition of *Armorial Families* is unlikely to be borne with legal authority.

I have his daughter's copy of the two volumes of the final, seventh edition, published after Fox-Davies's death, containing her bookplate by her mother. It also contains a number of manuscript notes and annotations in Moyra's hand-writing and references to a future edition. It would

appear that she had intentions of carrying on, or assisting to carry on, her father's work, as late as the 1940s, but nothing came of it. She almost certainly had a hand in the final preparations of the seventh edition because there are corrections to it concerning events which post-date the death of Fox-Davies.

Although *Armorial Families* was his major work it was not his first one. This was *The Book of Public Arms* produced jointly with Nell Crookes (his future wife) in 1894. In spite of her name appearing on the title-page one might be forgiven for thinking the work was solely by Fox-Davies. The whole of the introduction is written in the first person singular. Though there are detailed references to various people by name who have given help and assistance the only reference to Miss Crookes's major contribution is the following paragraph:

'My collaborator whose name appears upon the Title-page, and who has been responsible for the illustrations in the Volume has also assisted me in no small degree on other points connected with the book, and in matters which should have fallen entirely upon my shoulders; and for this I wish to tender my acknowledgements.'

The book consists of fifty-eight pages of text and one-hundred and thirty pages of illustrations, usually five coats of arms per page. Allowing for her contribution to the text and the whole of the illustrations, bar two by George Eve, it would appear that three quarters of the work was by Nellie Crookes. In the second edition published in 1915 her name disappears entirely from the title-page. The work is expanded but the additional drawings are by another hand. By this time, of course, the couple were married. Whether the removal of her name was by her wish or his is not clear.

The first edition received a scathing revue from the *Pall Mall Gazette*:

'At first sight we were led to expect an antiquarian and heraldic treat from the handsome volume produced by Messrs. Jack of Edinburgh and edited by Mr Arthur Charles Fox-Davies. A survey of the book, however, reveals it to be a pretentious and preposterously stupid work. —— We gather that the illustrations which not only form the largest but also the most valuable portion of the work, are due to M.E.B. Crookes (the sex is doubtful), whose name appears with that of Mr. Fox-Davies on the title-page. Mr Fox-Davies however assumes all the credit and responsibility of the work. Mr Fox-Davies has already issued two massive volumes on those most useless and misunderstood adornments, Crests [These were his revised editions of Fairbairn's Crests and Mottoes], *and announces another elephantine bantling to be christened 'Armorial Families'.*

He really must have upset someone severely to have received a revue like that.

In 1899 a book entitled *The Right to Bear Arms* appeared under the pseudonym of 'X'. It was based on a series of articles first published in the *Saturday Review* by the same author and later enlarged upon in the *Genealogical Magazine*. It is a scholarly dissertation on the history of the subject and the modern use and abuse of arms. A reviewer in the *Ex Libris Journal* Vol. IX notes, in referring to the *Saturday Review* articles:

'He not only treated the matter generally but went into particulars and cited numerous instances of peers, baronets and others who are at the present time using arms to which they are not entitled. These emphatic statements led to much discussion and comment, and the writer received no small measure of abuse for his temerity in thus attacking men with notable and high-sounding names.'

It must also be said the writer received a number of threats of writs for his allegations. In the preface to the book he states '*I have nine threats of libel actions in my drawers at the moment for indicating that different people are using arms without a right thereto. And not one of the nine can show a vestige of a right.*'

The game is rather given away later in the same article in the statement,

'We, of course, note in this connection the similarity of style and argument to that contained in the introductory portion of the 'Family Armorial' and the 'Book of Public Arms' – in fact, all these works are akin.'

The book was indeed written by Fox-Davies and I have his personal copy in which he lists on the back page twenty-nine people to whom he sent presentation copies including his father and a number of notable people in the world of heraldry – Sir Arthur Vicars (Ulster), Sir James Balfour Paul (Lyon), G.E. Cockayne, H.F. Burke (Somerset Herald), George Marshall (Rouge Croix) and Everard Green (Rouge Dragon). All the acknowledgements are also tucked in the back.

In his letter of thanks Sir Arthur Vicars says:

'I am much obliged to you for sending me a copy. I have already got copies for friends and on some of whom I hope your dissertations will have a wholesome effect!'

Sir James Balfour Paul says, slightly more grudgingly:

'It seems quite well done and gives information which is to be had, so far as I know, nowhere else. I trust it may have some good effect on the public'.

These two gentlemen served as the only two Presidents of the old Ex Libris Society, Sir Arthur Vicars from 1896–1900 and Sir James Balfour Paul from 1900–04.

In 1904 Fox-Davies produced another classic work *The Art of Heraldry*. It is based on an earlier German work, *Heraldischer Atlas* by Herr Hugo G. Strohl. Fox-Davies was originally invited to edit an English translation. It was obvious that some changes would need to be made to adequately cover English heraldry and with the publishers backing a much enlarged version was produced, plentifully illustrated in colour and black and white, under his own name.

The author invited contributions from other experts in the field but was scrupulous in distinguishing between their work, his own and that of Herr Strohl. The additional illustrations are largely by George Eve, C. Helard and John Forbes Nixon. He particularly pays tribute to Helard's contribution and also to that of his sister, Grace Muriel Fox-Davies who undertook the translation from the German. She was obviously something of a linguist because as well as translating from the German she also translated a number of works from Danish. This she did under the pseudonym of Grace Herring, her paternal grandmother's maiden name, apparently, at Charlie's insistence, to avoid confusion with her brother's works.

He ends his introduction to the book with a typical Fox-Davies remark:

'To the several others who promised me assistance but have failed to carry out their promises, I can only say that I would gladly have accepted the will for the deed, had it been possible to put the will into type.'

In 1909 Fox-Davies produced another major work – *The Complete Guide to Heraldry* based on *The Art of Heraldry* but omitting most of the continental heraldry. The title-page says the illustrations are mainly by Graham Johnston but a number of them are by Helard. It was revised by Charles A. Franklyn in 1949 and ran through five editions until 1961. It underwent a further major revision by the late John Brooke-Little, Norroy and Ulster King of Arms in 1969 to bring it heraldically up to date. In his preface Brooke-Little deals briefly with some details of Fox-Davies's family and this brings me to Fox-Davies's own heraldic position.

Brooke-Little states:

'In 1886 arms were granted to Thomas Edmond Fox-Davies with limitation to him and his descendants and the other descendants of his late father Charles —.'

However this was not the case. Arthur Charles Fox-Davies does not use personal arms until 1905. In that year he commissioned his well-known bookplate from Graham Johnston (see fig. 11). There is no mention of Fox-Davies arms in any of the early editions of *Armorial Families*, not even in the fifth edition of 1905. Later editions show the arms of Fox-Davies, drawn by Helard, under the heading 'Fox-Davies of Coalbrookdale' (H. Coll. 26 December 1905) a clear indication that the arms were only granted in that year.

The picture is further complicated in that arms were granted to Fox of Coalbrookdale one day later (H.Coll. 27 December 1905). 'Per pale argent and gules, three foxes sejeant counterchanged and for a crest, on a wreath of the colours a demi stag winged gules collared argent.' Granted to be placed on a monument to the memory of the late John Fox, and to be borne by his issue. John Fox died in 1893 leaving only two daughters, one of whom was Fox-Davies's

mother. This meant that Thomas Edmond Fox-Davies, following the death of John Fox, would bear the Fox arms in pretence with those of Fox-Davies and his issue, would quarter the arms following the death of their mother. I have seen both Grants of Arms which are currently in the possession of his grandson-in-law, Colonel Tony Molesworth.

There is a bookplate for Thomas Edmond Fox-Davies based on Johnston's bookplate for A.C. Fox-Davies but showing the Fox arms in pretence (see fig. 12). In the amended plate, as well as altering the name, the Lincoln's Inn arms in top centre are removed and replaced with a stylised rose. The Fox arms are in outline only, the tinctures not being delineated. It is not known whether the alterations were undertaken by Johnston or possibly by Helard. He also had his own plate modified for use by his elder brother, John and his younger brother, George, with suitable cadency marks.

Fig. 11 Original drawing for bookplate of Arthur Charles Fox-Davies by Graham Johnston, 1905

Fig. 12 A.C. Fox-Davies' bookplate modified for his father showing the arms of Fox in pretence

In a letter to his mother Charlie ends up by saying: *'I'm glad you like the new Armorial Families, Father will be in the next one. I enclose a proof of his bookplate. The prints will be ready very soon I hear.'* It is undated, he never seems to date his correspondence to family, but was written sometime in January or February 1906. In another letter to his father around the same time he explains the family's armorial position in detail and the part he played in securing the Grant (see Appendix II).

I have Graham Johnston's original drawing for Fox-Davies's bookplate. It would appear that alterations had to be made to it after completion. At the bottom on the left-hand side is the figure of a dragon couchant. On the right hand side the figure has been cut out and a backing piece inserted on which is a wyvern couchant. Query, what was it replacing? Also, the cadency mark of a crescent in centre chief, indicating a second son has been stuck on over something else. Presumably some other incorrect cadency mark. The design is strong and bold, a typical Johnston plate with plenty to interest the observer.

The pen and ink drawing is large measuring 19.2 × 13.5 cms (see fig. 11). On a canted shield are the arms: Sable, a demi sun in splendour issuant in base or, a chief dancettee of the last, surmounted by a helmet and the crest, on a wreath of the colours a demi dragon rampant gules collared or, holding in the dexter claw a hammer proper. Beneath is the motto 'Da fydd'. The whole set within a pillared arch with foxes in each top corner and surmounted by the arms of Lincoln's Inn – Azure, semi of mill rinds or, on a canton or a lion rampant purpure. According to Fox-Davies in his *Book of Public Arms* – second edition (1915) the Lincoln's Inn arms are borne without lawful authority so it is somewhat ironic that he who abhors the illegal use of arms should allow them on his bookplate.

The crest of a red dragon is obviously to denote his Welsh origins but what of the hammer? Is it, as seems likely, intended to represent his iron-making ancestry or, might I suggest, tongue in cheek, to beat up those who use arms illegally or simply to smash their achievements? The drawing is signed at the bottom of the left hand pillar with a monogram 'GJ' under a crown and the date 1905.

On 20 December 1921 Fox-Davies was granted a badge in the form of 'a crown vallery gules' which can be seen in his daughter's bookplate, H103, produced in 1930.

From various pieces of correspondence which I have seen Fox-Davies does not seem to have been very adept at managing his financial affairs. I have already alluded to his

problems at the time he was called to the Bar when he was seeking a loan from his mother to pay his fees.

In a written account of his life, written during the first World War he says: *'Why, I have no idea, but the keeping of family records has had a certain amount of fascination for me. It can hardly be the result of my work, for my work was really the consequence of my inclination. Looking back I regret it for I have no sort or manner of doubt that had I put into some other channel the same hard work that I have expended on my books, I might and probably should have made a greater financial success of my life. But, on the other hand I might not have travelled quite so far as I have got in one or two directions.'* (See Appendix III).

It was not so much that he was not earning money as that his income was erratic, depending on fees for services rendered, from the law and from his books. From time to time his outgoings exceeded his incomings.

Even at the end of his life his position does not seem to have been improved. In a letter to his mother in December 1927 dealing with various family matters he turns to the subject of his finances yet again. After mentioning a few minor debts he goes on:

'Then there is my blasted Income Tax- one Government Department says I owe £1,100, a different Government Department at a different address says I owe £932 and has filed a Bankruptcy Petition against me (they say nothing will be made public if I pay them another cheque) that is the same debt only two different methods of collecting it. That was served on me two days ago but I should imagine that means they are no longer holding arrest over my head. A week ago a third Government Dept. butted in for Super-Tax, as if I had ever in my life earned £2,000 a year

He goes on to seek a loan of £150 of which he proposes to send £100 to the Inland Revenue and use the rest to pay his household bills and keep a roof over his family.

Fox-Davies died only five months later on 19 May 1928. Although he had made a simple will on the occasion of his marriage, and which still exists in the family papers, presumably it could not be found at the time and he was deemed to have died intestate. Letters of Administration were granted to his widow on 10 December 1928. The gross value of his estate was recorded as £738-19s-od and the net value of his personal estate was recorded as nil.

He is buried in a separate grave in Coalbrookdale churchyard the other side of the path from the Fox-Davies family tomb containing the remains of his parents and siblings. Nellie's ashes were later placed in the same grave (see fig. 5).

Miss C. Helard, fl. 1895–1932

C. Helard was 'born' in 1895. It was the pseudonym that Mary Ellen Blanche Crookes, used for her heraldic drawings and bookplate designs. Its origins have never been satisfactorily explained and are not known in the family. The only suggestion I can make is that 'Helard' is an anagram of herald and 'C' may stand for Crookes but this is by no means certain nor is the reason for using a pseudonym.

Between 1893 and 1895 she signed her drawings 'M.E.B. Crookes'. She produced all the illustrations for *The Book of Public Arms* in 1894 and many of the illustrations for the first edition of *Armorial Families* in 1895. For the latter she was paid up to £1 for a full page illustration showing nine coats of arms. Her income for 1894, detailed in the back of an old exercise book, was over £40 for illustrations for *Armorial Families* alone. By the standards of the time, with her other work, this would have been a reasonable income for a single lady.

C. Helard was 'born' a man, in 1895, and had a sex change about 1899. This will come as a surprise to most of my readers but is clearly borne out by the evidence and reference to the *Genealogical Magazine*. In Volume I, 1897, we find a report on the Ex Libris Society's sixth annual exhibition, 10–11 June 1897 almost certainly compiled by the editor, Charles Fox-Davies, where he states:

'*Another pleasing exhibit was a frame of seven plates executed by Mr C Helard who is certainly one of the best heraldic bookplate designers of the present day. The pick of his plates was a small one of W. C. Bernard.*' (H005)

This was a generous tribute to a young artist who had just started her bookplate career but of course Fox-Davies had a close working relationship with Helard and had, no doubt, developed a personal relationship as well by this time. It is interesting that he chose the Bernard plate to highlight because it was by no means the best of the plates she produced around that time but it is possible that the Bernards were related to Fox-Davies which may account for the selection.

Again a year later, in 1898, there is a reference in the same magazine (volume II, p. 458) to designs 'drawn by Mr C. Helard' for the second edition of Armorial Families. The article goes on to say:

'*Perhaps the best in that Edition is the plate of James Nield Sykes (HO13) which is reproduced here in as much as it is an excellent example of the work of Mr C. Helard, a large number of whose designs have of late come into our hands.*'

In the *Ex Libris Journal*, June 1899 as part of a series on modern bookplate designers we find 'No. 16 Miss C. Helard' with no explanation in between for the 'sex change.' Later references in the *Genealogical Magazine* and in the *Ex Libris Journal* all refer to Miss C. Helard. It should be noted, however, that all her signed plates are signed 'C. Helard' with no prefix.

In that June 1899 article, the Journal editor W.H.K. Wright wrote:

'*We have now the pleasure to introduce to the notice of our readers a young lady of considerable attainments – Miss Helard now residing at Castletown in the Isle of Man. This lady is scarcely thirty years of age but she has done some good work. About six years ago, at the instigation of a friend, she turned her attention to heraldic drawing, and, soon becoming interested in the work, she contributed from time to time drawings in outline to illustrate heraldic articles in the magazines. Two years later she applied herself to the designing of heraldic bookplates, her first effort being that of Dr John Irwin Palmer.*'

There follows, what the author of the article believes to be, a complete list of her bookplates, between 1895 and 1899, by year – thirty-seven plates.

It is interesting that the account gives nothing away about her work with Fox-Davies. It is hard to believe that the author was unaware of it or of Helard's real name. There must have been a number of people 'in the know' but her wider anonymity seems to have been preserved. She carried on correspondence in the name of Helard from her home address and I have a letter addressed to 'C. Helard' saying her account had been passed for payment so she may even have had a bank account in the name of Helard.

In the December 1900 issue the same author lists another eight plates, Rt. Hon. Arthur J. Balfour PC (H035), Ethel F. Beckett (H043), George Fredrick Saul (H011), Marcia, Countess of Yarborough (H052) and four which were illustrated: Sir Thomas Sutherland (H051), William Ridley Richardson (H050), A. Edmund Fraser (H045) and Graeme Harrison (H046) and goes on to say:

'It is with much pleasure that we call attention to these plates, which are decidedly good, and are in every way an advance upon those previously executed by the same artist. The only fault we can find, if it be a fault, is in the uniformity of the designs, but they being chiefly heraldic plates there was not much scope for original and independent treatment. The only pictorial in the group that of Ethel Beckett (H043) shows clearly that Miss Helard is capable of good work quite apart from heraldry.'

Almost certainly 'the friend' referred to in the first article is her future husband, Charles Fox-Davies, who was busy writing his *Book of Public Arms* in 1893. It was published the following year complete with M.E.B. Crookes' drawings and I have her personal copy signed on the fly leaf- 'Nellie Crookes, June 1894' (see fig. 13).

The only other contemporary account we have of Helard's work occurs in the *Genealogical Magazine* in the issue for January 1902. As it is written by the editor, who is now her husband, we must again allow for some matrimonial bias.

'There are at the present time a large number of bookplate designers whose work is before the public, but some few stand head and shoulders above the remainder. Mr G.W. Eve and Mr C.W. Sherborn both have their admirers who place them at the head of the list of present day designers, and most people would readily admit that the plates of both artists are unique in their excellence as examples of the two differing methods of handicraft which each respectively adopts, (etching and engraving) The designs of Miss Helard places her above the majority of the remainder of her competitors, and are well worthy to rank next to the work of Eve and Sherborn. (See fig. 14).

Miss Helard is young and should she continue her work will doubtless far surpass in the future the point of excellence she has already reached. But she has never been at any very great pains to secure work, having done but little more than has 'come her way'. The number of her plates therefore is not very great – probably fifty or so – and as she has many interests in life, it is not upon quantity that her reputation exists.

It was, as is often the case, quite by chance that Miss Helard turned her attention to bookplate designing and heraldic drawing; but having taken it up, she set herself to learn the rules of heraldry and determined to adhere to them rigidly in her work. Herein lays one great excellence in Miss Helard's work: she knows armory and its laws; she knows what liberties may and may not be taken, and the result is that none of Miss Helard's plates are disfigured by glaring heraldic errors. This can be said about the work of few, if any other, designers, with the single exception of Mr Eve.

For the work and for the designs of this master of his art Miss Helard has always had a great admiration, and his influence upon her work is very marked in some of her earlier plates. It is perhaps less so at the present time, when a greater knowledge and a wider experience both of art and of heraldry have produced a greater confidence in her own powers, and as a consequence a distinctive originality of her own. Few designers have shown such a marked and rapid improvement in the quality of their work. The majority of the plates which Miss Helard has designed have been engraved, but she herself has etched some, having studied etching with Mr Percy Thomas, who exhibited at the last Exhibition of the Painter Etchers Society a characteristic portrait of Miss Helard, which had been executed whilst she was engaged in working under his supervision.' (See frontispiece).

As the author writes from close personal knowledge the content is interesting. Quite clearly, at this time, she is not

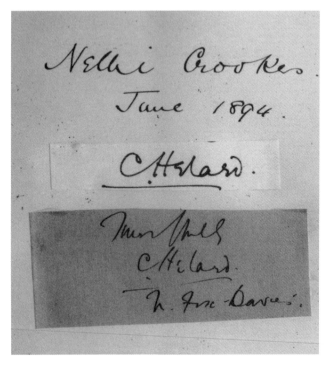

Fig. 13 Nell's various signatures, as a single lady, as a bookplate designer and as a married lady

(a)

(b)

(c)

Fig. 14 Three bookplates for Richard Southcote Mansergh by
(a) George Eve, (b) C.W. Sherborn and (c) C. Helard

seeking work but simply responding to demand. It was interesting to discover, later, that a number of her commissions came from Canada and North America. Is there a hint in the *'should she continue in her work'* that she might be losing interest, or has too many other things in her life or, being recently married no longer had the economic necessity of earning her own living, a man was expected to support his wife in those days. Certainly her output of bookplates falls off after 1902 apart from a slight resurgence in 1905. To say that *'none of Miss Helard's plates are disfigured by glaring heraldic errors'* is going a bit too far. A number of her plates can be criticised in heraldic terms, (see below).

Reference is made to Helard's admiration for the works of G.W. Eve and she was not his only admirer. Fox-Davies was a great fan and frequently alluded to the excellence of his work in his various writings. Eve's influence on Helard's work can in fact be seen throughout her bookplate career, particularly in her best designs.

A comparison of the two artists, Eve and Helard, is quite revealing. It must be remembered that at the time Helard began her bookplate career, aged twenty-five, Eve was forty and firmly established and Sherborn, at sixty-four, was 'the grand old man' of the heraldic bookplate world (see fig. 15).

There are a number of features of Eve's work which are characteristic of him, some of which Helard adopted and adapted for her own use:

1. Eve eschewed the use of hatched lines to denote tinctures, particularly colours, and rarely, if ever, used them. His view is clearly expressed in his *Heraldry as Art* published in 1907:

'Tinctures are sometimes indicated by means of lines and other marks, a system which arose in the beginning of the seventeenth century and was derived from the line tints which had long been used in engraving to distinguish contiguous spaces from each other, and used in that way were valuable and unobjectionable because they were under control. When, however, a colour meaning was given to the lines the designer was no longer able to restrict their employment to where they were artistically useful, but must use them throughout or not at all. And the latter is, on the whole, the most satisfactory way. On flat spaces, if the lines are sufficiently pronounced to be legible, they may lead the eye in a direction that is not helpful to the composition, and on modelled charges or crests they have a flattening and confusing effect that is very disagreeable.'

Eve, instead of using linear hatching tended to use a decorative design for the field (see George Viner's plate fig. 15) or the charges (see James Charles Getting's plate fig. 15) in order to enhance the overall design. Helard followed these views in a number of her plates (see Neville, H070) and also favoured a type of 'pargetting' for the field or background. This decorative background or 'diapering' as it was called had its origins in medieval times where it was used, as a design, as a darker shade on top of a colour, leaving no doubt of course as to what the colour should be.

Fox-Davies in his *A Complete Guide to Heraldry* whilst discussing hatched lines and their variations states:

'It is unlikely that any change will be made in the future, for the use of tincture lines is now very rapidly being discarded by all good artists in this country.'

It was a rash statement because he was only really referring to Eve and Helard. Sherborn adhered to the linear convention with only rare exceptions such as his George Viner plate. All other heraldic artists of the period used conventional hatching and time has proved Fox-Davies wrong as the system is still in use today.

It was in the 17th century that a Jesuit monk, Father Silvester Petra Sancta devised a system of hatched lines, in various directions to denote particular tinctures before the days of colour printing. The details can be obtained from any standard book on heraldry. Even after the introduction of colour printing the system continued to be used for engraving on silver or glass or for any black and white design such as a bookplate.

Whilst in artistic terms there may have been some argument for abandoning hatching, in purely functional terms there was none. The purpose of heraldry is identification and if one cannot differentiate one tincture from another the purpose is lost.

It is interesting to note that in his illustrations for the first edition of *Armorial Families* (1895) Eve uses tincture lines for all the drawings no doubt at the behest of the author who seems to have changed his tune subsequently.

In a number of Helard's plates there are discrepancies between the design and the blazon as shown in *Armorial Families*. The lack of tincture lines in some of her plates with quartered arms has made identification difficult particularly if the full quarterings are not shown, or the arms not recorded at all, in *Armorial Families*.

2. Eve objected to the convention that said that the helmet of a gentleman should face sideways, in profile because, he said, it gave a flat two dimensional view to the crest. Instead, he favoured turning the helmet to a three quarter position draped over the shield and with the crest turned

Fig. 15 Four bookplates by George Eve illustrating his style

accordingly this gave a much more artistic three dimensional view (see James Getting's and William Richard Castle's plates fig. 15). He tended also to use one type of helmet, namely a 15th century tilting helmet which proved very effective.

Helard adopted the turning of the helmet but to a lesser extent and not always with the same dramatic effect because she usually omitted to turn the crest as well leaving it, rather awkwardly, slantwise across the helmet. She also favoured a variety of helmets, again, not all of which were successful in artistic terms.

3. Eve also had firm views about the use of the wreath or torse which was originally a soft silken wreath perched like a crown on top of the helmet and in which the crest sat. It was there to hide an unsightly join as well as to add colour to the pageantry. The crest and wreath would only have been used during a tournament never in battle where it would have added unnecessary weight to an already weighty outfit. Eve said of the wreath:

'It should always be treated as a silken favour wreathed around the helmet and not as a rigid support for the crest, to which it is merely a decorative accessory.'

He suggested that a phrase used regularly in the blazoning of arms, 'on a wreath of the colours' was responsible for the wreath being use as a board to support the crest which was then balanced precariously on top of the helmet in a very ungainly manner. Helard was guilty of this offence in some of her designs (see Cave-Orme (H017), Darcy Wilson (H025) and Christie (H026)) in which the wreath either extends beyond the curve of the helmet and seems to rest on the mantling or sticks out straight like a board.

Originally the wreath was a soft silken rope comprising the two chief tinctures of the arms which was wound round the base of the crest to conceal the join with the helmet. Hence Eve's view of the matter is correct.

4. The shape and positioning of the shield was of interest to Eve and he advocated adapting both to the needs of the artistic design of the arms being depicted. The traditional pointed or 'heater' shield often created difficulties in its lower portion, particularly if a complicated impaled coat is required (see Sir James de Hoghton's plate fig. 15). Here Eve overcomes the problem by broadening the base of the shield. Helard failed to appreciate this in her plate for Sir David Dale (H007) with dire consequences for the design.

Tilting the shield at an angle, with the helmet draped over the sinister corner, can produce a nice effect which Eve much favoured and which was also used by Helard.

5. Eve's view of the mantling or lambrequin was that it was there as an adjunct to the design and allowed the designer free rein to do with it as he will. It originated in the short mantle that was attached to the helmet and hung a little way down the wearer's back to protect him from the sun. It later became confused, due to the profusion of mantling, with the surcoat which covered the whole body.

In English heraldry it is usually depicted cut to ribbons as though slashed in battle, which allows for much artistic licence. It tended to follow the design used in gothic tracery in dividing and sub-dividing in groups of three which curved and interlaced in a foliate pattern. Both Eve and Helard used this design effectively often, in Helard's designs, ending in a tri-lobed form seen at its most stylised in her very first plate, for John Irwin Palmer (H001).

6. Both Eve and Helard, more than other designers of their day, favoured producing their designs in more than one size and more than one colour. The favourite colour was, of course, black, followed by dark brown, reddish brown and then a lighter shade of brown presumably at the whim of the owner. In the case of Helard's plate for Gery Milner-Gibson-Cullum (H068), it is produced in a variety of shades including red.

Helard began her designs with ink outline drawings (Soames, H040) or pencil sketches (Davidson, H092a) which were submitted to the client for comment. From this the design was produced in ink and watercolour usually black or sepia which was given to the engraver. Helard did not engrave her own plates. She initially used Charles Laurie and later the firm of Downey, Alfred Dyer Downey and his son Alfred James Downey. These engravers also did much work for Fox-Davies's *Armorial Families* which is probably where Helard came into contact with them.

Among the Helard archive is an unfinished drawing of the arms of Sir David Stewart for inclusion in *Armorial Families* (see fig. 16) with a rather cheeky leopard's face with its tongue poking out. It must have been commissioned before they were married and still living apart. It has been folded into four, no doubt for posting and there is a pencilled enquiry to the right of the head, 'do you like his tongue out?' Underneath is the reply, 'Yes, if you can draw it well, otherwise better leave it shut.' She must have decided she could draw it well because the two leopards appear in the book with their tongues out. David Stewart was Lord Provost of Aberdeen from 1889–95 and was created a Knight Bachelor in 1896. His arms are: 'Or, a fess chequey azure and argent between two leopards faces in chief gules and a galley sable in base, flagged of the fourth.' No mention of tongues sticking out.

Helard studied etching under Percy Thomas RE (1846–1922) and later etched some of her own designs. Her first attempt was the plate for George Fredrick Saul (H011a) which is printed in sepia. There is also an engraved version in black (H011) which is much crisper, the etching having a softer outline.

Percy Thomas was a painter and etcher of landscapes, genre scenes and portraits. He studied at the Royal Academy School as well as under James McNeill Whistler. Whistler taught him to etch. Thomas exhibited at the Royal Academy from 1867 and was elected a member of the Royal Society of Painter-Etchers and Engravers in 1881. He etched a portrait of Helard in 1900 and exhibited it at The Painter Etchers Society Exhibition in 1901. The copy shown as the frontispiece to this volume is the personal copy to Helard, signed by the artist and endorsed bottom right 'With kind regards to Miss C. Helard'.

A number of Helard's plates in the archive are printed on India paper. These are engravers proof prints and are often signed in ink by the artist showing approval of the final version. This was a common practice for etchers and engravers as John Vinycomb notes in his book 'On the Processes for the Production of Ex Libris' – 1894:

'The engraving being completed, the surface of the block is inked very lightly with printing ink and a piece of India paper, or any fine paper of similar quality, being laid upon it, an impression is taken by rubbing the paper with the burnisher until it is fully printed. From this proof the engraver can judge whether any alterations are required and what improvements can be effected.'

Once the engraver was satisfied the final proof would be submitted to the designer for approval.

A number of the early plates in the Helard archive bear pencilled prices on the back, probably as an 'aide memoire' for the artist. I am assuming it is the price charged to the client. Her starting price in April 1895 for Dr Palmer (H001) appears to have been £6-6-0 but she notes she received a cheque for £3-6-0. Was this part or full payment, or her share after she had paid the engraver? The charge to Kirkpatrick-Howat (H009) the following year was only £2-10-0. In 1897 prices rose; Robert Aikenhead (H016) was charged £4-0-0 and Rev. J. Vicars Foote (H019) £4-10-0.

In 1899 prices went 'up market' into guineas. Hubert Wilson (H041) £6-6-0, a drawing submitted to a 'Mr Wilson' in 1895 had been refused but it is not clear if it is the

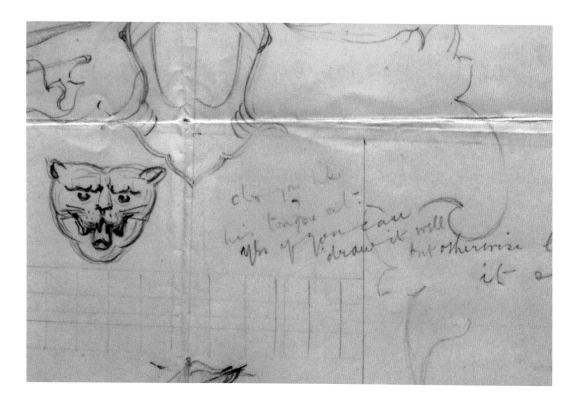

Fig. 16
Unfinished sketch, arms of Sir David Stewart by C. Helard showing leopard's head with tongue protruding

same Mr Wilson. In 1900 prices rose again, A. Charles Pirie (H049), £7-7-0 and A. Edmund Fraser (H045), £8-8-0. There are no prices noted after 1900. To get a comparison with the cost of living in those days it should be noted, for example, that an employee on the railway was paid less than £1-0-0 a week with which to support a wife and family, and I have it on good authority (my grandmother) that it could be done.

It would appear that she sometimes sent samples of her work to potential clients for comment or selection. On the back of the plate for Robert Aikenhead (H016) there is the pencilled note: 'I prefer this style G.A.C. Orme'. The same year G.A. Cave-Orme received his plate (H017) in the same style and at the same price. To some extent, of course, the price would vary according to the amount of work involved and the charge made by the engraver (see below).

There is a letter from Helard in the Downey archive dated 3 December 1905, the year the Penton plate was produced:

Dear Mr Downey,

Mardon plate – This is very good indeed and I have no fault to find. Will you please send it to Mr Goulding to await instructions.

Are you getting on with the tiny Cust plate? I have another one ready for you when that is done.

Enclosed is a cheque for £4-5-0 for the Penton plate. Let me know why you charged me more for this plate than the others so that I may know in future.

Yours truly
N. Fox-Davies

From this it would appear that about half the cost to the client was the cost of engraving. It is also noted that here she is corresponding under her married name of Nell Fox-Davies (see fig. 13). The Mr Downey addressed would almost certainly have been Mr Downey senior, Alfred Dyer Downey who at that time would have been forty-nine. His son, Alfred James was then aged twenty-three.

A slightly earlier letter to Downey dated 14 November 1905 and referring to the large Lionel Cust plate (H077) shows her attention to detail:

Dear Mr Downey,

Many thanks for last proof. It wants a bit of altering, but I must say first how much I like the engraving of it. Both my husband and I think it is excellent. I told you I wanted the motto in Old English did you overlook this? The first word is 'Qui', be careful over the letters at the bottom of the plate 'M.V.O.' and 'F.S.A.'

Can you add a bit of curl of hair to the back of the lion's head. I have added them to my sketch and it is an improvement. Also to make the escallops black and to show the waves on the fountains is an improvement. The crescent is charged with a mullet.

I have gone over the proof very carefully and pencilled it with what I want done. Will you let me have another proof of this. It will be a splendid plate. Shall have some more work for you shortly.

Yours truly
C. Helard
N. Fox-Davies
I will send you a cheque for Latter plate (H078) in a day or so.

It is interesting to note the double signature (see fig. 13). The postscript could be an indication that she was 'not in funds' at the time of writing, otherwise why not include the cheque and save extra postage.

There is no doubt that, at its best, Helard's design work is as good as any produced by Eve and better than some produced by Sherborn but her work is not consistently good and occasionally weak and lacking in impact. I would cite as some of her best work:

Fredrick Dundas Harford (H088)
Philipp Schey de Koromla (H090)
Charles Stuart Forbes (H091)
Lord Wharton (H094)
Viscount Lascelles (H099)
Reginald Monckton (H101)
Alexander Spreckley Raworth (H102)
Charles Wilbraham Perryman (H032)

Amongst her poorer plates I would note
Wickham-Legg (H108)
Alfred Middleton Rickards (H089)
Anthony Browning Coote (H109)

In the April 1902 issue of the *Genealogical Magazine* there was an Editorial Notice announcing exciting developments for the following month, no doubt, intended by Fox-Davies, to try and boost circulation. It included the gift, each month, of one-hundred copies of a personal book-plate to a selected subscriber. Readers wishing to be recipients were requested to send full particulars of what may be required in the way of design. Quarterings were not to exceed six in number. Applications were to be accompanied by an order for the magazine for the next twelve months except for past subscribers who had already purchased a year's subscription. The gift was conditional on sufficient use being made of the prints to entitle them properly to rank as bookplates.

The designs were to be undertaken by Graham Johnston and Miss C. Helard. Those by the latter were half tone blocks from wash drawings. Helard produced eight plates over the following eighteen months: H060, H061, H062, H063, H064, H067, H069 and H072. They do not rate amongst her best works, being rather inferior in quality but this may be due to the production process.

As well as her bookplates and illustrations for her husband's many books she also undertook other heraldic work. In 1911 she produced thirteen drawings of the arms of City Livery Companies to be included in a series of fifty cigarette cards issued by the Imperial Tobacco Company. The letter from the company, dated 30 November 1911, acknowledging receipt of the drawings goes on to say:

'With regard to the 'Badges' we regret we are unable to entertain these at present, and we are returning the four specimen sketches herewith.'

Fig. 17 Original drawings by C. Helard showing four Royal Badges – 'Crowned Portcullis', 'The Rose-en-Soleil', 'The Sun Burst' and 'Rose and Pomegranate' (see back cover for colour plate)

The four 'Badges' are very fine watercolour drawings of Royal Badges which were in the Helard archive (see fig. 17) and on the back of each, in Helard's own hand, are historical details:

1. The Rose and Pomegranate
This badge is a conjunction of the red rose of England and the pomegranate of Granada; the latter, one of the badges of Queen Katherine of Aragon. The conjoined badge was used by Henry VIII and Queen Katherine and by their daughter Queen Mary.

2. The Sun-Burst
Although this badge has been attributed to Edward III it probably originated with Henry VII who made great use of it. He, of course, was known as Henry of Windsor and it is doubtless an attempt to punningly portray the name 'Windsor' by 'winds or' that is 'of gold'.
[The Sunburst crowned is the badge of Windsor Herald].

3. The Crowned Portcullis
This badge, a favourite one with the Tudors Henry VII and Henry VIII was used with and without the motto 'Altera Securitas' and is believed to be a pun on the name 'Tudor' a portcullis being a second door. Whilst this is probably a correct account of its origin it does not explain its use by the Beaufort line. [This is the badge used by Somerset Herald].

4. The Rose-en-Soleil
In this form we owe the badge to King Edward IV whose favourite badge it was. But in that form it is really a combination of two distinct badges. The white rose of York and the 'Sun of York' made famous by Shakespeare but which is traced back to Richard II.
[This is the badge used by York Herald].

The majority of her dated bookplate designs were undertaken in the ten years 1896–1905. Thereafter they trickle down to one or two a year no doubt as she is bringing up her young family. There is a slight resurgence in the 1920s but her last plates, in the 1930s are not of particularly good quality. She had given up having them engraved and resorted entirely to half tone blocks.

It is interesting to note that she never, apparently, designed a bookplate for her husband nor used one herself. The bookplate for her daughter, Moyra (H103), was only produced in 1930 and she never produced a bookplate for her son. As a soldier travelling widely and frequently he was, probably, never in one place long enough to build up a library requiring a bookplate. Although she enjoyed the design work, see her letter to Downey, she does not appear to have been very interested in the use of bookplates for herself or her family.

A study of her plates by design, date and signature is revealing. Her first plate, for Palmer in 1895, is a panel armorial signed with initials in lower case 'ch'. The following year her output shot up to fourteen plates. Eleven of these were panel armorials, all signed 'C. Helard' but only one, Sir David Dale, was dated. Two were simple armorials unsigned and one, for Fletcher was a seal armorial initialled in lower case. Of the ten plates produced in 1897, all but one were simple armorials unsigned; the odd one was a panel armorial for Carlyon-Britton which was signed and dated. In 1898 there were nine plates, five were simple armorials unsigned and four were panel armorials, two signed and dated and two signed The pattern seems to be that her simple armorials were unsigned and her more elaborate panel designs were signed and dated.

A full list of her plates, year by year, to date was published in the *Ex Libris Journal* in June 1899. Thereafter

Fig. 18 Mrs Nell Fox-Davies (C. Helard) in later life *c.*1920

her output, up to 1932, of signed and dated plates was almost entirely signed panel armorials; but included five pictorial plates, two seal plates and one simple armorial for Ferrier (H111) in 1932. Also included in this period are all the undated plates in Section V which were found in the Helard archive.

Whilst Nellie Crookes was an active and busy person all her life she seems to have had a shy and retiring nature. She did not seek publicity but preferred to stay in the background. Many of her bookplate customers were related to each other by kin or marriage and, no doubt, commissions came as a result of seeing examples of her work. Photographs of her are rare (see fig. 18).

In 1969, in reply to a query from Bookplate Society member, Horace Jones, Mary Spencer Fox-Davies, daughter of John Fox-Davies, Charlie's brother, wrote:

'First of all I am able to solve your problem, because 'C. Helard' was my aunt by marriage, the wife of my Uncle, Arthur Charles Fox-Davies. It was the name she took, I understand, even before she married when she started doing her beautiful designs. She was truly a very gifted woman and needless to say a tremendous help to my Uncle in his work.

I am afraid, however, I am not able to help you with the names of her engravers. I phoned my cousin, who is their daughter, [Moyra] and she was so interested to hear about my letter from you. She said that unfortunately all her old records and papers are away in store and have been for many years (she and her husband have moved about a good deal). She was so sorry she could not help you any further but when she is able to get hold of them again, and if she does find anything that would be of interest to you I will let you know.'

I find it surprising and intriguing that even a query that reached her daughter did not result in the revelation of why she chose the name of Helard and what the derivation might have been.

Descendents of the family living today know a great deal about her husband, Charlie, but very little about her. They were unaware that she used the name of 'Helard' or even that she produced bookplates. Consequently whilst I have learnt a great deal about other members of her family, I feel that the real personality of Helard still eludes me.

By her works shall you know her.

C. Helard – Dated Bookplates, 1895–1932

Helard's plates are mainly armorial and of two types, simple armorials where the achievement may be full or partial and panel armorials where the achievement is usually complete and enclosed within a decorative panel surround. Those, in this section, are either dated on the plate or from lists in the *Ex Libris Journal* 1895–1908 and arranged in alphabetical order within year. Measurements, which are in centimetres with the vertical side first, are the overall design size and not the plate impression size. Unless otherwise stated all imprints are in black

He served for a time as Surgeon Major to the 3rd Middlesex Volunteer Artillery and was visiting Medical Officer to the Military Hospital, Tooting. He was Honorary Surgeon to the Distressed Gentlefolk's Aid Association and Senior Anaesthetist at the Great Northern Central Hospital. In spite of all this he found time to conduct a general practice from the medically fashionable district of Harley Street, West London. He was made an Officer of the Most Excellent Order of the British Empire, (OBE) following its creation in 1918.

H001 1895 John Irwin Palmer 11.4 × 6.9 cms

This is Helard's first attempt at a bookplate and as such is a credible effort. The punning arms are well displayed. Looked at critically, however, there are a number of design faults. Although she uses the three quarter view of the helmet favoured by Eve, with good three dimensional effects, the crest is two dimensional and flat sitting at an awkward angle across the helmet. The embowed arm is not 'grasping a palm branch and palmer's staff in saltire' it is holding the staff but the palm branch is floating behind the fist. The mantling is strangely lobulated, a style which she favoured later on in a modified form. The plate is signed with initials 'ch' in the bottom right hand corner. The engraver's initials 'CL' for Charles Laurie are in the left.

ARMS: Argent, on a chevron embattled, counter-embattled, plain cottised, between three palmers staves, all sable, as many scrips of the first, buckled and tasselled or.

CREST: On a wreath of the colours, on a dexter mailed arm embowed, grasping a palm branch and a palmer's staff in saltire all proper, an escallop or.

MOTTO: 'Palma virtuti' – The palm of merit.

Dr John Irwin Palmer was the eldest son of John Palmer (1829–80) of Eliot Place, Blackheath and his wife Harriet Elizabeth Adams. He was born in 1852 and studied medicine at Guy's Hospital, London qualifying as a member of the Royal College of Surgeons (MRCS) in 1881.

H001

H002 1896 (George Barbour) 11.8 × 7.5 cms

A panel armorial which does not use tincture lines, this example is shown before naming. The helmet and crest are shown in traditional sideways view with the exception of the base of the helmet which is turned three quarters so that it fits over the shield, a trick which Helard uses in a number of her plates. The mantling looks more like foliage rather than a tattered cloak but it is effective artistically. It is signed 'C. Helard' at bottom right.

ARMS: Argent, on a saltire guttee d'eau between two garbs in pale and two escallops in fess vert, an escallop of the first (Barbour), impaling, Party per fess nebuly azure and or, in chief a sword argent point downwards and in base a galley sable under sail argent, flags and pennons gules (Macfie).

CREST: On a wreath of the colours, in front of a mount vert thereon a Cross Calvary argent, a garb fesswise or.

MOTTO: 'Nihilo nisi Cruce' – With nothing but the Cross.

H002

George Barbour MA, JP, DL was born in 1841, the only son of Robert Barbour of Sawmillfield, Glasgow and his wife, Janet, daughter of William Flemming. He was educated at Harrow and Trinity College Cambridge and was called to the Bar by the Inner Temple in 1865.

He married 20 October 1869, Caroline, daughter of Robert Macfie, of Dreghorn Castle, Midlothian, Scotland. They had one son, Robert, and six daughters.

He was a Justice of the Peace and Deputy Lieutenant for the county of Cheshire and High Sheriff of the same county in 1890. He was an honorary major in the Earl of Cheshire's Yeomanry and lived at Bolesworth Castle near Chester. He died on 3 November 1919.

H003 1896 William Henry Battie-Wrightson
10.6 × 7.4 cms

This is an extremely complicated impaled coat which has been depicted in minute detail. There is always a problem trying to fit two crests onto one helmet and the solution to divorce both from the helmet seems to work. The three quarter position of the helmet is an improvement on that in H002. Signed at bottom left hand side.

ARMS: Quarterly 1 and 4, Or, a fess engrailed chequey argent and azure, between four griffins heads erased, three in chief and one in base of the second (Wrightson), 2 and 3, Sable, a chevron argent between three goats statant of the last, each charged with two pallets gules, on a chief or, a demi man affrontee the dexter hand holding a club in bend between two cinquefoils gules (Battie), impaling Barry of ten argent and azure six escutcheons, three, two and one sable, each charged with a lion rampant argent (Cecil).

CRESTS:
1. On a wreath of the colours, on a rock proper a unicorn rampant resting the sinister foreleg on an escutcheon or charged with a griffin's head erased azure (Wrightson).
2. On a wreath of the colours, a heron statant proper holding a fish in its beak (Battie).

William Henry Battie-Wrightson was born William Henry Thomas in 1855. He was the eldest son of the Reverend Charles Edward Thomas, rector of Hewsworth, Yorkshire and his wife Georgiana Mary. She was the third daughter of Colonel Henry Hely Hutchinson of Weston, Towcester, and his wife, Harriet, the eldest daughter and co-heiress of William Wrightson of Cusworth.

In 1884 he married Lady Isabelle Georgiana Katherine

H004

H003

Cecil the eldest daughter of William, 3rd Marquess of Exeter. He assumed the name and arms of Battie-Wrightson, by Royal Licence, in 1891.

He was appointed Justice of the Peace and Deputy Lieutenant for the county of Yorkshire and High Sheriff for the county in 1900. He died in 1903.

H004 1896 Charles Bellairs 8.5 × 6.0 cms

A well balanced design signed, in the border, at bottom right. Note the widening of the shield at the base to accommodate all the quarterings. The omission of tincture lines possibly provides a greater legibility of the charges. There is something rather odd in the fact that the arms shown in the last three quarterings were all granted on the same day, 7 April 1785. It cannot be a coincidence. Presumably an ancestor was keen to accumulate quarterings onto his family escutcheon.

ARMS: Quarterly of six: 1, Ermine, a lion rampant gules, on a chief engrailed sable a leopard's face between two cross crosslets fitchee or (Bellairs, 16 May 1786), 2, Argent, a cross gules, on a chief azure an eagle displayed between two cross crosslets fitchee or (Bellaers 9 March 1782), 3, Quarterly gules and azure, a lion rampant argent ducally crowned and in chief two garbs or (Bellaers 13 April 1776), 4, Azure, a chevron erminois between three griffins passant or (Lea 7 April 1785), 5, Gules, a fess vairee erminois and azure between three escallops argent (Foote 7 April 1785), 6, Argent, a fess and in chief, a lion passant gules (Walford 7 April 1785).

CRESTS:

1. Out of a mural crown or, a demi lion rampant gules, holding between the paws a cross crosslet fitchee or.
2. On a wreath of the colours, a horse's head couped argent, in the mouth a leaf of oak proper.

MOTTO: 'Virtus tutissima cassis' – Virtue is the safest helmet.

William Charles Bellairs of the Red House, Dachet, Berkshire was born in 1861. He married, in 1887, Alexandra Elizabeth Mortimer Ritchie, daughter of H.N. Ritchie. He died at the age of only thirty-eight in 1898 leaving one son Thomas Claud M'Kenzie Bellairs, born in 1892, who later became a lieutenant in the Royal Navy.

H005

H005a

H005 1896 William Cecil Bernard 7.5 × 5.3 cms

A full panel armorial, with three quarter helmet, crest slantwise across it and motto over. Signed bottom right corner. It has typical Helard trilobed mantling. Note the punning nature of the arms. A print of this plate with the name scroll blank was published in the *Ex Libris Journal*, June 1899. The arms, in this form, are attributed to a family called *Barnard* so it would appear that they maybe used here without lawful authority. This is further borne out by the fact that they do not appear in any addition of *Armorial Families* under Bernard. However the crest is listed in *Fairbairn's Crests*, revised edition (1986) by Laurence Butters, as belonging to Bernard, Huntingdon and the motto is given there as 'Nisi paret imparat' – unless he obeys he commands.

ARMS: Argent, a bear rampant sable muzzled or.

CREST: A demi bear rampant muzzled and collared or.

MOTTO: Bear and Forbear.

Captain Isaac Bernard, his wife Mary and son William Cecil, born in 1865, lived at Cromwell House, Huntingdon having bought the property in 1876. It is a large detached house with grounds built in 1810 on the site of an earlier house in which Oliver Cromwell was born. Bernard was a retired sea captain who worked for the Peninsular and Oriental Steam Navigation Co. and who died in 1894. Shortly afterwards Helard came to lodge with Mrs Bernard, possibly as a companion to the widow, and during that period designed this plate for her son William.

H005a 1896 (William Cecil Bernard) 7.5 × 5.3 cms

Identical to the above plate but without his name.

H006 1896 Sir Charles Buckworth-Herne-Soame Bart. 8.8 × 6.5 cms

A symmetrically well-balanced design on a diapered background. The use of a separate helmet for each crest works well but the positioning of the crests causes a problem. Being a baronet the helmets face forward and the Soame crest of a hawk would also have faced forwards if used on a helmet during a tournament. Here, oddly, it faces sideways across the helmet because that is the view normally shown of a crest. The problem is partially over come in the Buckworth crest by turning the man's head into three quarter view. The plate is signed with initials 'Ch' at bottom right.

ARMS: Quarterly 1 and 4, Gules, a chevron between three mallets or, a canton argent for difference (Soame), 2 and 3, Sable, on a chevron between three cross crosslets fitchee argent, an ermine spot (Buckworth). In the centre of the escutcheon there is his badge of rank as a baronet.

CRESTS:

1. Upon a wreath of the colours, a lure argent garnished and lined or, thereon a hawk of the last charged upon the breast with a cross crosslet for difference (Soame).

2. Upon a wreath of the colours, a man's head helmeted, the visor open, all proper. (Buckworth).

Charles Buckworth-Herne-Soame was born on 29 May 1830 the son of Charles Buckworth-Herne-Soame, who was the third son of the 6th baronet, and his wife Hannah, daughter of Richard Proctor of Ironbridge.

He studied medicine at St Bartholomew's Hospital, London and qualified as a member of the Royal College of Surgeons (MRCS) and, also, became a licentiate of the Society of Apothecaries (LSA).

He married, in 1855, his cousin Mary, daughter of Richard Fellowes Proctor and thus became Helard's uncle by marriage. He succeeded his uncle as 9th baronet in 1888. He had a general medical practice in Dawley, Shropshire and was surgeon to the 3rd Battalion, the Bedfordshire Regiment. He was a Justice of the Peace and a Member of the Shropshire County Council. He died on 26 March 1906.

H007 1896 Sir David Dale Bart. 9.9 × 6.7 cms

This plate which is generally well-balanced and uses tincture lines is, otherwise, poorly designed and suffers because of the impalement and the use of a spade-shaped shield. This distorts the placing of the lower two besants in the Dale arms. The canted shield with overlapping helmet almost obliterates the top charge on the Millbank arms. Signed and dated on right hand of name scroll.

ARMS: Azure, a swan argent between four besants, two and two, his badge of rank on the chief point (Dale), impaling, Gules, a saltire argent, guttee-de-poix between two lions heads couped in pale and as many roses in fess of the second (Millbank).

CREST: On a wreath of the colours, in front of two eagles heads erased and addorsed proper, an escutcheon azure charged with a besant.

MOTTO: 'I byde my tyme'.

David Dale was born on 11 December 1829, the second son of His Honour David Dale of the Honourable East India Company Service, Judge of the Murshedabad City Court, and his wife, Ann Elizabeth, daughter of the Reverend George Douglas.

He married in 1853 Ann Backhouse, daughter of Edward Robson and widow of Henry Whitwell. She died in 1886. He married again, in 1888, Alice Frederica, the eldest daughter of Sir Fredrick Millbank.

He was a Justice of the Peace and Deputy Lieutenant for the County Palatine of Durham and High Sheriff there in

H006

H007

1888. He lived at West Lodge, Darlington. He was created a baronet on 13 July 1895 and died in 1906. He was succeeded by his son, from his first marriage, James Backhouse Dale who followed in his father's footsteps as a Justice of the Peace and Deputy Lieutenant for County Durham.

H008 1896 John Robert Fletcher 6.6 cms diameter

A seal armorial with canted shield on a mural background with restrained use of mantling. Name and motto is around circumference. It is initialled 'ch' at lower right.

ARMS: Argent, on a cross invected between, in chief two pheons and in base two arrows points downwards, all sable, three pheons in fess of the first.

CREST: On a wreath of the colours, in front of a naked arm embowed holding a long bow, two arrows in saltire points downwards all proper.

MOTTO: 'Forti nihil difficile' – To the brave nothing is difficult.

John Robert Fletcher was born on 19 August 1855 the eldest son of James Fletcher and his wife Charlotte, daughter of Robert Leake. He married, 29 August 1884, Ellen, daughter of Thomas Tonge.

He was appointed a Justice of the Peace for the County Palatine of Lancaster and lived at Kearsley, Stoneclough, Lancashire and The Uplands, Whitefield near Manchester.

H009 1896 Reginald Kirkpatrick-Howat
8.0 × 3.8 cms

A plain armorial without helmet or mantling with the motto above in the Scottish manner.

ARMS: Quarterly 1 and 4, Argent, a saltire azure between three mullets in chief and flanks and an owl in base gules, on a chief of the second three cushions or, all within a bordure gules for difference, 2 and 3, Or, a chevron nebuly between three eagles displayed vert, a bordure azure for difference.

CREST: On a wreath of the colours, a dexter armed hand holding a dagger in pale distilling drops of blood proper.

MOTTO: 'I mak sicker'.

Reginald Kirkpatrick-Howat of Mabie was the son of Robert Kirkpatrick-Howat of Mabie a Justice of the Peace and Deputy Lieutenant for the county of Kirkcudbright,

and his wife Amelia, the only child and heiress of Edmund Blewitt of Llantarnum Abbey, Monmouthshire.

He married, 26 January 1888, Mary Elizabeth, daughter of Philip d'Arcy Ker of Waldridge Manor and Ker's Hill, Maryland, U.S.A. They had one son, Robert Mabie Kirkpatrick-Howat, born 9 January 1890, and three daughters. The family estate was at Mabie, Dumfriesshire.

H010 1896 John Ward Procter 7.5 × 5.0 cms

A plain armorial, shield and crest with motto over, using tincture lines. It is unsigned.

ARMS: Or, three Passion nails in pale sable, two and one.

CREST: On a wreath of the colours, a sleeved dexter hand in pale holding a hammer in bend sinister proper.

MOTTO: 'Fit via vi' – The way is made by labour.

John Ward Procter came of a long line of physicians stretching back into the 18th century. He studied medicine at Charing Cross Hospital, London and qualified as a member of the Royal College of Surgeons (MRCS) and a licentiate of the Society of Apothecaries (LSA) in 1856. He became a licentiate of the Royal College of Physicians (LRCP) in 1873. He had a medical practice in Shifnal, Shropshire and was assistant surgeon to the 14th Shropshire Rifle Volunteers. He was also district surgeon to the Great Western Railway Company.

One of his brothers, James Proctor also qualified as a doctor in Edinburgh and was in practice in Ironbridge. His sister was Ann Blanche Proctor, Helard's mother, so this plate was designed by Helard for her uncle. The various members of the family seemed to vary in the spelling of their name, ending it 'er' or 'or'.

As these arms are not listed in any edition of *Armorial Families* it is doubtful if they were borne with lawful authority. Fox-Davies is aware of their use because he refers to them in an account of his family's genealogy saying – *'they use for arms – Sable, three passion nails argent'*. Notice the change of tinctures. In a letter to his father in 1906, (see Appendix II), Fox-Davies talks about obtaining Grants of Arms for the Crookes and Proctor families, implying that they do not already possess them legally.

H008

R. Kirkpatrick-Howat.

H009

JOHN WARD PROCTER. M.R.C.S.

H010

H011 1896 George Frederick Saul 7.4 × 5.7 cms

An engraved plate with full armorial, profuse mantling and motto over. There is a name scroll bottom left 'Ex Libris George Frederick Saul of Brunstock' and it is signed bottom right 'C. Helard'.

ARMS: Per chevron gules and argent, two chevronels counterchanged, in centre chief a label of three points for difference.

CREST: On a wreath of the colours a swan statant, wings addorsed proper, collared and chained argent.

MOTTO: 'Fideli certa merces' – There is a sure reward for the faithful.

George Frederick Saul was born in 1863 the son of Silas George Saul and his wife Sarah. His mother died whilst George was still a small boy.

The family owned the Brunstock Estate near Carlisle in Cumbria. His father was a solicitor and George was brought up by a retinue of servants including a cook, governess, nurse and groom. He went on to become a solicitor like his father. He married, in 1898, Eleanor Maud Wybergh.

H011a

H011a 1896 George Frederick Saul

As above but the plate is etched. This is Helard's first attempt at an etched bookplate. The effect is not as sharp as the engraved version and less well defined in areas although this could be partly due to the fact that the plate is printed in sepia rather than black. The mantling is more compact and the signature slightly larger.

H012 1896 Nathaniel Spens 9.1 × 6.2 cms

A full panel armorial within a beaded border with motto over and name scroll below. It is signed in the border, bottom right.

ARMS: Quarterly 1 and 4, Or, a lion rampant gules within a bordure of the last charged with eight roses argent, in the dexter chief point a heart ensigned with an Imperial Crown both proper (Spens), 2 and 3, Gyronny of eight or and sable (Campbell of Glendouglas). The whole within a bordure invected, parted per fess ermine and azure for difference.

CREST: On a wreath of the colours a hart's head erased proper.

MOTTO: 'Si Deus quis contra' – If God is for us who is against us.

The bordure overall was a standard method of differentiating between different members of the same family in Scottish heraldry, akin to cadency marks in England. His

H011

brother John Alexander Spens bears the same arms but the bordure invected is parted per pale ermine and azure for difference.

Nathaniel Spens was born 27 April 1850 the fifth son of William Spens, actuary, of Glasgow and his wife Janet, daughter of Walter Cook WS of Edinburgh. He married, 26 July 1882, Emily Jessie daughter of William Connel of Solsgirth. They had two sons and three daughters and the family home was at 13 Queensgate Terrace, London S.W.

H013 1896 James Nield Sykes 8.2 × 6.3 cms

A panel armorial with full achievement within a plain border. The motto is above and the name scroll is below. It is signed on the bottom right hand border.

ARMS: Argent, three chevronels sable between two fountains in chief proper and a bugle horn stringed in base of the second, on the honour point, a fleur-de-lis azure for difference (sixth son).

CREST: On a wreath of the colours a demi man in profile proper charged on the breast with a fleur-de-lis azure, holding in his dexter hand a fountain and resting his sinister hand on a whelk shell sable.

MOTTO: 'Aye ready'.

James Nield Sykes was born in 1825 the sixth son of John Sykes of Lindley, Huddersfield and his wife Charlotte, daughter of John Bray.

He married, 26 April 1852, Ann daughter of John Fox of Daisy Lea, Lindley, Huddersfield and had three daughters.

He was a Justice of the Peace for Huddersfield and the West Riding of Yorkshire and lived at Field House, Lindley, Huddersfield. He died in 1903.

H012

H013

H014 1896 James Williamson-Napier 8.4 × 5.9 cms

A full panel armorial within a decorative border. The helmet is in three quarter view with the crest slantwise across it. It is signed in upper right hand ribbon of name scroll.

ARMS: Party per pale, gules and azure, on a bend argent three crescents of the second and, in the sinister canton, a spur rowel of the third.

CREST: On a wreath of the colours a man's head adorned with laurel proper.

MOTTO: 'Virtute gloria parta' – Glory is obtained by valour.

James Williamson-Napier (formerly James Williamson) representative of Napier of Kilmashaw was born 25 January 1855 the eldest son of Thomas Williamson MD of Leith, Edinburgh and his wife Mary Ann, daughter of Francis Howden of Edinburgh.

He married, 23 March 1885, Albertina Elizabeth daughter of J.D. Schott of Arnheim, Holland. They had two sons and two daughters. He died in 1911.

H015 1896 Sir Thomas Wright 8.6 × 5.8 cms

A full panel armorial with plain border showing the inevitable problem of the crest sitting sideways on a knight's helmet. It is signed outside the panel bottom left 'C. Helard del.' and bottom right, 'C. Laurie sc.'

ARMS: Or, on a pale gules a cross botony fitchee argent, on a chief azure a pale ermine charged with a rose barbed and seeded proper, between two besants.

CREST: On a wreath of the colours, upon a rock a falcon's head erased proper holding in its beak a cross botony fitchee in bend, argent, and charged on the neck with a rose as in the arms.

MOTTO: 'Tam arte quam marte' – Rather by art than might.

Thomas Wright was born 15 February 1838 in Northampton, the second son of Joseph Wright and his wife Jane daughter of Robert Prestidge.

He married, on 10 June 1862, Georgiana daughter of Peter Roberts of Northampton. He trained as a solicitor and had a distinguished career in Leicester. He served as a Justice of the Peace for the county and was Mayor of Leicester in 1887–8 and again in 1891–2. He founded the Children's Hospital in Leicester in 1888 and was largely instrumental in obtaining a large extension to the Borough of Leicester in 1890 for which he received the Honorary Freedom of the Borough. He was knighted (Knight Bachelor) in 1893 after which he headed up the firm of Sir Thomas Wright and Son, Solicitors.

He lived at The Hollies, Stoneygate, Leicester and died on 5 August 1905.

H016 1897 Robert Aikenhead 8.4 × 5.8 cms

A simple armorial with motto ribbon. The helmet with spiracles in the visor is one of Helard's favourites, shown here in three quarter view without turning the crest thus leaving it sitting slantwise across the helmet. The crest is too large for the helmet leaving the wreath drooped awkwardly over it. The order for this plate was originally placed in April 1895 so it was some time coming to fruition. The price charged was £4 and pencilled on the back are the words 'I prefer this style G.A.C.Orme' (see H017).

ARMS: Argent, three acorns slipped and leaved vert, two and one, two flaunches gules each charged with a thistle slipped and leaved or.

CREST: On a wreath of the colours, a demi man affrontee, holding in his dexter hand a branch of laurel slipped and fructed all proper and resting his sinister hand on a chaplet of oak fructed proper.

MOTTO: 'Rupto robore nati' – We are born from a broken oak.

Born in 1822, Robert was the second son of John *Akenhead* and his wife Abigail nee Harrison. In 1886 he assumed the original Scottish spelling of the family name. He was a Justice of the Peace for the North Riding of Yorkshire.

He married, 23 November 1864, Frances Anne, eldest child of Joseph Davidson of Greencroft Park, Durham. They had one son, Frank, and one daughter.

Fox-Davies had noted that Robert was using a simpler version of the above arms without the charged flaunches. Although registered in Lyon's register they did not apply to Robert. He later matriculated the arms in the form shown above. The family lived at Otterington Hall, Northallerton, Yorkshire.

H014

H015

ROBERT AIKENHEAD.

H016

George Alington Cave-Orme.

H017

George Hudson Earle.

H018

H017 1897 George Alington Cave-Orme

7.0 × 6.0 cms

Cave-Orme had been shown a range of Helard's styles and had chosen one similar to the Aikenhead plate above. This time although the base of the helmet is in three quarter view the top is turned so that it is facing left and thus accommodating the crest but again it is too small leaving the wreath overhanging.

ARMS: Argent, a chevron between three escallops in chief and a dolphin naiant in base all gules.

CREST: On a wreath of the colours, a dolphin naiant argent charged on the body with two escallops gules, between two branches of coral of the last.

George Alington Robinson was born in 1867 the eldest son of William Thomas Robinson. He assumed the name of Cave-Orme by Royal Licence in 1888 under the will of his cousin Charles Cave-Orme sometime High Sheriff of Rutland.

He married, in 1891, Ida Ventry daughter of William Kennedy of New South Wales. He was a member of the Middle Temple; LLM, BA (Cantab), and BA (University of Melbourne).

H018 1897 George Hudson Earle

7.3 × 6.0 cms (excluding name)

A simple armorial plate with typical Helard mantling and motto below. It has a three quarter facing helmet with the crest sitting awkwardly across it.

ARMS: Gules, a fess between three shelldrakes two and one and as many escallops one and two; on a shield of pretence sable, two bars dancetty argent.

CREST: On a wreath of the colours, in front of two spears in saltire proper, a lion's head erased or, charged with two escallops fesswise gules.

MOTTO: 'Magna est Veritas' – Great is the Truth.

George Hudson Earle was born on 27 May 1851 the eldest son of George Foster Earle and his wife Sarah Theodosia daughter of John Hudson.

He married, 20 July 1883, Susanna Catherine Elizabeth, Baroness de Reede de Ter Aa who died 24 February 1896. They lived at Rocklands, Torquay, Devon and 3 Lancaster Gate, London W.

H019

H020

H019 1897 The Reverend J. Vicars Foote M.A.

7.2 × 5.6 cms (excluding name)

A simple armorial plate with full achievement and motto.

ARMS: Per chevron, argent and or, three martlets azure.

CREST: On a wreath of the colours, a martlet azure charged on the breast with a cross humette or.

MOTTO: 'Spes mea Deus' – God is my hope.

John Vicars Foote was born on 26 March 1852 the only child of the Reverend Richard Gorges Foote and his wife Maria Louisa daughter of John Swire.

   He studied at Worcester College, Oxford, BA 1877; MA 1883. He was ordained, in Winchester, in 1879 and was later vicar of East Cleveland, near Bristol, 1886–99. He owned an estate in Ireland, Seskin Ryan, Co. Carlow.

   He married, 18 January 1888 Margaret daughter of William Hallam Elton, Commander RN.

H020 1897 William Edward Gibb (no example)

Although the plate is listed in the *Ex Libris Journal* in 1899 no example has yet come to light. This illustration of the arms is taken from the fourth edition of *Armorial Families* (1902).

ARMS: Gules, a cubit arm erect grasping an arrow in bend sinister, point downwards between four mullets, in cross, or.

CREST: On a wreath of the colours arising from a wreath of cinquefoils vert a stag's head or, couped gules attired argent.

William Edward Gibb was born on 16 March 1849 the son of Thomas Augustus Gibb of Lancaster Gate, London and Shanghai.

   He married, on 5 June 1873, Frances Elizabeth daughter of Francis Tunnicliffe. She died in 1896. They had one son, Francis William Gibb born 4 September 1879.

   He married again in 1898, Lydia Maude daughter of William Hill of Maldon, Essex.

   He served as a Justice of the Peace for Essex and lived at Pyrgo Park, Romford, Essex.

H021 1897 John Cole Kemsley

7.0 × 5.3 cms (excluding name)

A plain armorial plate with the motto below. The helmet is poorly designed in relation to the crest and wreath which bear little or no relation to the top of the helmet.

ARMS: Or, on a mount in base vert, a man in armour holding over his dexter shoulder a battleaxe, head downwards, proper, on a chief arched, per pale sable and gules two lions passant, counter passant, argent.

CREST: On a wreath of the colours, on a mount vert a demi zebra proper, gorged with a collar gemmel or, resting its sinister foreleg on an esquire's helmet proper.

MOTTO: 'Semper paratus' – Always ready.

John Cole Kemsley was the eldest son of John Nicholas Kemsley and his wife Elizabeth Kathleen daughter of Patrick Waterman Cole.

He married, 23 April 1885, Elizabeth Jopling daughter of John Robert Brickon.

H022 1897 Thomas Mackenzie

7.9 × 5.7 cms (excluding name)

A simple armorial plate, nicely designed using tincture lines and typical Helard mantling.

ARMS: Azure, a stag's head caboshed, between the antlers an antique crown or.

CREST: On a wreath of the colours a dexter arm embowed, the hand grasping a garland of laurel proper.

MOTTO: 'Virtute et Valore' – By virtue and valour.

Thomas Mackenzie was born on 18 March 1848 the third son of William Mackenzie and his wife Jane daughter of William Thomson of Knocklands.

He married, 30 October 1877, Emily daughter of Edwin Holt of Rosehill, Worcestershire. He was a Justice of the Peace for the counties of Banff and Morayshire and Deputy Lieutenant of Morayshire. He lived at Dalhuaine House, Carron, Strathspey and died in 1915.

H023 1897 Rear Admiral Edwin John Pollard

8.8 × 6.4 cms

This example is an engraver's proof signed in ink by Helard. It is a simple armorial using tincture lines with motto above and name scroll below. Signed and dated bottom right of shield and was engraved by Downey.

ARMS: Azure, a chevron ermine between two crosses fleury in chief and a sea lion's head erased in base (Pollard), impaling, Quarterly 1 and 4, party per pale indented, argent and vert, three demi lions rampant, those in chief gules and or respectively and the one in base party per pale indented of the same (Whitshed), 2 and 3, Party per chevron argent and vert, three hinds trippant proper (Hawkins).

CREST: On a wreath of the colours, a stag trippant proper, holding in its mouth two wheat ears or, gorged with a collar pendant therefrom a cross fleury of the last.

Note: This is the description given in the first edition of Fox-Davies's *Armorial Families*. In later editions it is altered (? corrected) to 'a stag trippant proper gorged with a mural crown and charged on the shoulder with a cross fleury or' (see H132).

Edwin John Pollard was born on 21 April 1833 the second son of Edwin Pollard of Theresa Place, Gloucester, High Sheriff of the county, and his wife Eliza daughter of Henry Hughes of Tewkesbury.

He entered the Navy as a cadet in 1846 (aged thirteen) and had a distinguished career. He fought in the Crimea and was awarded the Crimean and Turkish medals, 1854 and 1855, with a clasp for Sebastapol. He commanded a gunboat in China 1857–62 and was awarded the China medal with two clasps for Canton (1857) and Taku Forte (1860).

He married, 18 November 1862, Renira daughter of Sir St Vincent Keene Hawkins-Whitshed and his wife Elizabeth daughter of Lord Erskine. He lived at Haynford Hall, Norwich, was Justice of the Peace and Deputy Lieutenant of the county. He retired from the Navy in 1885 and died 15 September 1909.

John Cole Kemsley.

H021

THOMAS MACKENZIE.

H022

H023

H024 1897 Philip William Poole Carlyon-Britton

8.7 × 6.1 cms

A full panel armorial with name and date scroll, 1897, below and a double motto scroll above. There is an impaled coat with two crests and no tincture lines. It is signed 'C. Helard' at right hand of name scroll and was engraved by Downey.

ARMS: Quarterly 1 and 4, quarterly or and gules, two lions passant in chief and as many mullets of six points in base within a bordure engrailed all counter changed (Britton), 2 and 3, Sable, a plate between three towers argent each charged with a cross crosslet gules, and for distinction in the centre chief point a cross crosslet (Carlyon), impaling, Sable, a plate between three towers argent each charged with a cross crosslet gules (Carlyon).

CRESTS:

1. On a wreath of the colours a lion's gamb erect and erased azure guttee d'eau between two mullets of six points azure (Britton).
2. On a wreath of the colours a demi lion rampant gules, ducally crowned or, collared argent, holding between the paws a besant and charged on the shoulder, for distinction, with a cross crosslet of then second (Carlyon).

MOTTOES:

1. 'Salute a tous' – Respect to all (Britton).
2. 'Turris tutissima virtu' – Virtue is the safest fortress (Carlyon).

Philip William Poole Britton was born on 13 October 1863 the elder son of Henry William Britton, of Caer Brito, Ashley Hill, Bristol, and his wife Hannah Canter, daughter and sole heiress of Benjamin Poole of Summerhill House near Bristol.

He married, 8 September 1886, Agnes Cassandra elder daughter of Charles Alfred Carlyon of Kirby Muxloe, Leicestershire and granddaughter of the Reverend Thomas Stackhouse Carlyon, rector of Glenfield, Leicester.

He assumed by Royal Licence, 29 April 1897, the surname of Carlyon in addition to and before that of Britton and the arms of Carlyon, with a cross crosslet in the centre chief point for difference, quarterly with those of Britton. This plate probably celebrates that event. His offspring were to bear the arms and crest of Carlyon without the distinction mark as they were blood relatives of the Carlyons.

He became a solicitor of the Supreme Court, Justice of the Peace for Middlesex and Deputy Lieutenant of

H024

H024a

Gloucester. He was a working colleague and friend of Charles Fox-Davies and wrote the short chapter on Heraldry and Numismatics in Fox-Davies's *The Art of Heraldry* and which was also reproduced in the *Genealogical Magazine*. He wrote numerous articles on numismatics and was President of The British Numismatic Society 1904–8 and 1910–14.

He served as a captain in the 3rd Battalion Royal Enniskillen Fusiliers and as a major in the West Yorkshire Regiment 1914–18. He served as High Sheriff for Middlesex and lived at Eversfield, Fishbourne, Chichester. He died 26 June 1938.

H024a MCMVIII Philip William Poole Carlyon-Britton 8.7 × 6.1 cms

This is the same plate as H024 but with alterations also undertaken by Downey. The date, 1897, has been changed to MCMVIII (1908). The arms, crest and motto of Britton have also been changed and are now:

ARMS: Quarterly or and gules, in the first quarter an anchor erect of the second, a bordure engrailed azure.

CREST: On a wreath of the colours, a lion's gamb erect, erased azure grasping in the paw a trident erect or.

MOTTO: 'A tuz saluz'.

The reason for these variations is not known but as Fox-Davies shows them in the later editions of *Armorial Families* he would have been satisfied that they were borne with lawful authority.

H025 1897 Darcy Bruce Wilson

6.0 × 4.5 cms (excluding name)

A simple armorial plate with tincture lines and motto. It is a proof copy signed in ink 'C. Helard'.

ARMS: Per pale argent and azure, on a fess cotised three lions gambs erased fesswise all counter changed. In the dexter chief quarter a wolf's head erased sable.

CREST: On a wreath of the colours, on a mount vert, a lion's gamb erased fesswise argent in front of a lion's head couped erminois.

MOTTO: 'Perseverando' – By persevering.

Darcy Bruce Wilson was born on 17 June 1851 the second son of John Wilson of Seacroft Hall near Leeds, Yorkshire and his wife Anna Maria Isabelle, daughter of Roderick Macleod of Cadboll MP.

He served as a captain and later honorary major in the Yorkshire Imperial Hussars. He was a member of the Inner Temple, and a Justice of the Peace for Yorkshire.

H025

Thomas Craig Christie
of Bedlay.

C. Helard.

H026

William Howard Curtis Galt.

H027

H026 1898 Thomas Craig Christie

7.0 × 5.8 cms (excluding name)

A simple armorial with three quarter facing helmet and motto over, using tincture lines. It is a proof copy signed in ink 'C. Helard'.

ARMS: Or, a saltire indented between four mullets sable, on a chief of the second three crescents argent.

CREST: On a wreath of the colours, a branch of holly leaved and fructed proper.

MOTTO: 'Sic viresco' – Thus I flourish.

Thomas Craig Christie was born on 6 September 1816, the eldest son of James Ramsay Christie, merchant of Glasgow and his wife, Mary daughter and co-heiress of Thomas Craig.

He married firstly, 15 February 1853, Catherine Campbell daughter and heiress of James Campbell, she died 4 February 1854; secondly, 14 February 1859, Anna eldest daughter of John Cross Buchanan by whom he had two sons and four daughters.

He was Deputy Lieutenant of Lanarkshire and served as a Justice of the Peace for the counties of Lanark, Dumbarton and Glasgow. He was a Commissioner of Supply and of Taxes and Property for Lanarkshire. He died in 1910.

H027 1898 William Howard Curtis Galt

7.5 × 5.5 cms (excluding name)

An engraved simple armorial using tincture lines which suffers from the same fault as that of John Cole Kemsley (H021). The crest and wreath are ill-suited to the helmet. They balance precariously on top, the helmet being too small for the crest.

ARMS: Azure, on a chevron between three garbs or banded gules, a man's head in profile couped below the shoulder proper wreathed of the field.

CREST: On a wreath of the colours, on a garb fessways or, banded gules, a man's head in profile couped at the neck, proper, wreathed azure.

MOTTO: 'Nihil melius virtute' – Nothing is better than virtue.

William Howard Curtis Galt was born on 9 June 1870 eldest son of William Howard Galt and his wife Sarah Ann daughter of George Moore.

He married in Paris in 1902, Josephine daughter of Larbalettre de la Tremouille. He qualified as a solicitor to the Supreme Court of Judicature, Ireland in 1910. He served as a lieutenant in the 4th Battalion Royal Irish Rifles 1914–18. He owned estates in Ballysally and Coleraine but from 1922 he lived in Montreal, Canada.

H028 1898 William Macadam-Smith

7.5 × 6.5 cms (excluding name)

A simple armorial plate with motto using tincture lines.

ARMS: Azure, in chief a drinking cup and in base a chess rook or, on a chief engrailed of the last a chess rook of the first.

CREST: On a wreath of the colours, in front of a dolphin hauriant or, three chess rooks azure.

MOTTO: 'Generosity with Justice'.

William Macadam-Smith was born 2 October 1860 the third son of James Smith of Benvue near Glasgow and his wife Ann, daughter of Robert Brown of Edinburgh.

He married 5 September 1883 Helena Jane daughter of Richard Greenshields Ross and had three daughters. He lived at Abbotsfield, Wivenscombe, Somerset and was appointed Justice of the Peace for that county in 1896. He later retired to Glasgow.

H028

H029 1898 John William Morkill

7.0 × 5.8 cms (excluding name)

A simple armorial plate with motto and titling.

ARMS: Vair, a pale nebuly sable between four martlets, two in chief and two in base or (Morkill), impaling, Per pale azure and sable, two hobbies close proper in chief and a sun in splendour in base or (Hobson).

CREST: On a wreath of the colours, a martlet or between two lilies argent stalked and leaved and slipped proper.

MOTTO: 'Be true'.

John William Morkill was born on 3 May 1861 the only son of John Morkill of Killingbeck near Leeds and his wife Mary only daughter of William Greenwood.

He had a Master of Arts degree, Oriel College, Oxford and was a Justice of the Peace for the West Riding of Yorkshire.

He married, 1 March 1889, Hannah, youngest daughter of Peter Hobson. They had three sons and a daughter and lived at Austhorpe Lodge near Leeds.

H029

H030 1898 Lord Newlands
8.5 × 8.0 cms (excluding name)

A plain armorial with supporters and a coronet of rank.

ARMS: Vair, on a chevron gules three besants or, a chief, gyronny of eight or and sable charged with his badge as a baronet of the United Kingdom. Supporters, on either side a dapple grey horse gorged with a ribbon and suspended therefrom an escutcheon gules charged with three besants in chevron. The shield is surmounted by his coronet of rank as a baron.

CREST: A bloodhound sejeant proper.

MOTTO: 'Aye ready'.

William Wallace Hozier was born 24 February 1825, the eldest son of James Hozier of Newlands and Mauldslie Castle in the county of Lanark and his wife Catherine Margaret daughter of Sir William Feilden Bart.

Following a career as a soldier in various Scottish regiments he became a business man and director of the Caledonian Railway Company. He was a Justice of the Peace and Deputy Lieutenant for the City of Glasgow and Vice-Lord Lieutenant for Lanarkshire.

He was created a baronet in 1890 and raised to the peerage as Baron Newlands of Newlands and Barrowfield in 1898. Possibly this bookplate celebrated that event. His younger brother, Sir Henry Hozier, was the father of Clementine, wife of Sir Winston Churchill.

He married, 1 August 1849, Frances Anne daughter of John O'Hara of Raheen, Co. Galway and had one son and three daughters. He died in 1906 and was succeeded by his son James Henry Cecil Hozier as 2nd baronet and 2nd baron. James had no children and so the title became extinct on his death in 1929.

H031 1898 Reverend Samuel Nunn 9.1 × 6.6 cms

A panel armorial with full achievement, signed and dated at right hand side of name scroll which reads – 'S. Nunn A.M. Coll. Div. Joh. Cantae. Rector de Lauton in Com. Cest.'. The plate is engraved and also known in process reproduction. This plate was reproduced in the *Ex Libris Journal*, June 1899.

ARMS: Azure, a saltire or, between a boy's head affrontee couped at the shoulders, around his neck a serpent, in chief proper two garbs in fess and a lion's gamb erased in base of the second.

CREST: On a wreath of the colours, in front of a saltire azure, a bull's head erased or.

MOTTO: 'Justi sicut astra lucebunt' – The Just shall shine as the stars.

Samuel Nunn was born on 14 September 1835, the sixth son of the Reverend William Nunn MA vicar of St Clements, Manchester and his wife Elizabeth eldest daughter of Philip Vaughan of Kidwelly, Carmarthen.

He was educated at St. John's College, Cambridge where he was an exhibitioner. He became rector of Lawton in Cheshire and was acting chaplain to the 1st Volunteer Battalion, North Staffordshire Regiment 1878–98.

He married, 8 October 1863, Eliza second daughter of William Williamson and had two sons. He lived at The Rectory, Stoke-on-Trent and died in 1921.

H032 1898 Charles Wilbraham Perryman
10.3 × 7.3 cms

A panel armorial with full achievement, motto over and name scroll under. Signed bottom right and dated bottom left. A complex coat with a nice punning allusion, perry = pear. It is known in black, brown and process reproduction. A print, direct from the copper plate, was issued with the *Ex Libris Journal*, June 1899. The plate was engraved by Downey.

ARMS: Party per pale ermine and azure, two bars indented each charged with three pears slipped all counterchanged.

CREST: On a wreath of the colours a wolf's head ermine erased gules, charged with a fess indented azure surmounted by two pear branches leaved, fructed and slipped in saltire proper.

MOTTO: 'Per ardua stabilis' – Steady in difficulties.

Charles Wilbraham Perryman was born on 9 August 1860. He was a Justice of the Peace for Southampton and lived at Bifrons, Farnborough, Hampshire. He was Lord of the Manor of Ardley in Oxfordshire and patron of that living. He married, 12 July 1884 and had three sons and two daughters.

Lord Newlands.

H030

JUSTI SICUT ASTRA LUCEBUNT

S. Dunn, A.M.
Coll. Div. Ioh. Cantar
Rector de Canton in Com. Cest.

H031

PER ARDUA STABILIS

Charles Wilbraham Perryman

1898

H032

57

H033

H033 1898 Lt. General Charles Pollard

5.5 × 5.0 cms

A small crest armorial with helmet and mantling. There is a motto over and name scroll below. It is signed bottom right.

CREST: On a wreath of the colours a hind trippant proper.

MOTTO: 'Deus pro nobis quis contra nos' – God is for us who can be against us.

Charles Pollard was born on 16 September 1826 the youngest son of William Dutton Pollard DL, JP, of Castle Pollard, County West Meath, Ireland. He was educated at the Honourable East India Company Military College and obtained his Commission in the Bengal Engineers in 1845.

He married, 1851, Maria daughter of Cornelius Cole of Pembrokeshire.

He joined the Bengal Sappers and Miners and served in the Punjab Campaign 1848–9 including the first and second sieges of Multan, the Battle of Gujerat and subsequent pursuit of Sikhs and Afghans to Peshwar. He held various engineering appointments until made Chief Engineer of the Punjab in 1879, a post which he held until his retirement in 1883 having reached the rank of Lieutenant General.

He died on 24 July 1911 aged eighty-five years.

H034 1898 Robert Standish Sievier 8.5 × 6.0 cms

An engraved panel armorial plate with full achievement, impaled canted shield with motto under and name panel below. It is signed faintly along lower right border.

ARMS: Party per pale or and sable, a fleur-de-lis between two mullets of six points in fess and in base two ostrich feathers in saltire all counterchanged (Sievier), impaling, Quarterly 1 and 4, Or, a saltire and a chief gules, on a

H034

canton argent a lion rampant azure (Bruce), 2 and 3, Argent, a chevron gules between three morions azure (Brudenell).

CREST: On a wreath of the colours, on a rock proper, a mullet of six points gules between two ostrich feathers argent.

MOTTO: 'Ne cede malis' – Do not yield to evil.

Robert Standish Sievier was born on 30 May 1850 the only son of Robert Moore Sievier and his wife Alicia Maria daughter of Henry Stephen Sutton.

He married, 24 September 1892, Lady Mabel Emily Louisa Brudenell-Bruce (by Letters Patent raised to the rank of a Marquis's daughter 1887), daughter of George John Brudenell-Bruce, eldest son of the 3rd Marquis of Ailsbury who died in 1858 before succeeding to his father's title, and sister of George William Thomas Brudenell-Bruce, 4th Marquis of Ailsbury. They had one son and two daughters and lived at Elston House, Shrewton, Wiltshire.

Sievier was something of an entrepreneur. He served in the army during the Kaffir, Zulu and Bantu Wars in the 1870s. On leaving the army he went on the stage with considerable success and later became a race horse owner. His horses were raced in many parts of the world including Australia, Africa and India again with considerable success. He bought a yearling filly at auction for ten-thousand guineas and named her Sceptre. This was the highest price paid for a yearling filly at that time. She made a further

H035

H035a

record by winning four out of the five classic races of the period.

In 1904 he retired from racing horses and founded his own newspaper *The Winning Post* which was also a success from the first issue. He went on to write several books and plays including his autobiography.

He died on 8 October 1939 aged eighty-nine years.

H035 1899 Rt. Hon. Arthur J. Balfour PC

8.5 × 6.2 cms

An engraved panel armorial, printed in brown, with full achievement using a canted shield and three quarter facing helmet but with crest facing forwards. The motto scroll is above and the name scroll below. It is signed and dated at right hand end of motto scroll.

ARMS: Argent, on a chevron engrailed between three mullets sable a seal's head erased of the first with a bordure of the second for difference.

CREST: On a wreath of the colours a palm tree proper.

MOTTO: 'Virtus ad aethera tendit' – Virtue tends toward heaven.

It was described in the *Ex Libris Journal* November/December 1900 when the reviewer remarks – '*In our thinking it is somewhat heavy and dark, the design not being sufficiently clearly defined*' – and ends with a rather curious statement – '*Copies of this interesting plate (first impressions) are*

available on application to Miss C. Helard, The White House, Ironbridge, Shropshire.' Surely if this was a commissioned plate it would not be for the artist to be distributing copies to all and sundry, but see H035a below.

In the first edition of *Armorial Families* the arms are given in italics without the bordure and the author comments – 'These are matriculated in *Lyon's Register* as the arms of Balfour of Balbirnie of which family the Rt. Hon Arthur Balfour is only a cadet.' But in the corrigenda at the beginning of the book is the note – 'the Rt. Hon Arthur Balfour has now rematriculated his arms since the entry under his name was printed.' Using a bordure is a well established method of distinguishing a cadet branch of a family in Scottish heraldry.

H035a 1899 Arthur James Balfour 8.5 × 6.2 cms

Same plate as H035 but with the name scroll altered to read plain 'Arthur James Balfour'. This plate was illustrated in the January/February 1901 issue of the *Ex Libris Journal*. In the commentary the author states – '*We understand that Mr Balfour has adopted the practice of having his books blocked with his name in lieu of pasting bookplates in them. He does not wish to be bothered with applications for his plate.*' Taken in conjunction with the comment under H035 above it may explain why Helard was distributing copies of the plate. It is possible that Balfour did not commission the plate but that it was a gift from the artist to this eminent statesman of his time.

H036

H037

The Balfours are one of the oldest families in Scotland. The Balfours of Balbirnie date back to the reign of Robert II in the 14th century. Arthur's grandfather was James Balfour MP the second son of John Balfour of Balbirnie and his father, James, succeeded to the family estate in 1847.

Arthur Balfour was born on 25 July 1848, the eldest son of James Maitland Balfour of Whittinghame, East Lothian and his wife Blanche Mary Harriet, second daughter of James Brownlow William Gasgoigne-Cecil KG, 2nd Marquis of Salisbury.

He was educated at Eton and Trinity College, Cambridge.

He was a prominent statesman in the late Victorian and Edwardian periods serving in many offices of state including Prime Minister 1902–5. He was showered with honorary doctorates from most of the universities in England and Scotland. He was a Fellow of the Royal Society, awarded the Order of Merit in 1916 and created Knight of the Garter in 1922, the same year as he was given an earldom.

He never married and died on 19 March 1939 being succeeded by his brother as 2nd Earl Balfour.

H036 1899 John Henry Chalmers 9.0 × 7.0 cms

An engraved panel armorial with full achievement, the motto scroll above and the name panel below. The addition of the word 'Armiger' would seem tautological. Signed and dated at the end of the motto scroll. This plate was reproduced in the *Ex Libris Journal*, June 1899.

ARMS: Argent, a fess between, in chief a demi lion rampant between two fleur-de-lis and in base a falcon rising, all gules.

CREST: On a wreath of the colours, a falcon wings addorsed proper, semi de lis, between two quatrefoils, all gules.

MOTTO: 'Quid non, Deo Juvante' – What may not be performed under the favour of God.

John Henry Chalmers was born on 26 August 1849, the second son of the Reverend Thomas Smith Chalmers, formerly of Stafford and afterwards Torquay, and his wife, Eliza, daughter of Thomas Ward of Port Hill, Shrewsbury.

He married, 11 April 1888, Emily Frances, second daughter of William Sylvester JP of Stafford. They had two sons and the family lived at Holcombe, Moreton Hampstead, South Devon.

H038

H038a

H037 1899 John Maurice Coppen 8.7 × 6.5 cms

A panel armorial with full achievement within a decorative border, the motto over and the name scroll below. It is signed and dated at the right hand end of the name scroll.

ARMS: Azure, a chevron invected between two boars heads couped in chief and a demi gryphon couped in base or.

CREST: On a wreath of the colours, out of the battlements of a tower proper, a demi gryphon or, holding between the claws a saltire azure.

MOTTO: 'Copia sine penuria' – Plenty without want.

John Maurice Coppen was born in 1850, the second son of John Coppen of Lenham, Kent and his wife, Margaret, daughter of Maurice Jones of Aberystwith.

He married, 21 June 1872, Emmie, only daughter of Thomas William Boyden. They had one son and three daughters and lived at Ascot, Berkshire.

H038 1899 Arthur G. Soames 9.0 × 6.2 cms

A full panel armorial within a beaded border. There is typical Helard mantling with the motto over and the name scroll below. The helmet and crest are in line with a well placed wreath. Signed and dated outside the border bottom right. The plate is engraved but also known in process reproduction.

ARMS: Gules, a chevron or between three mallets erect of the second.

CREST: On a wreath of the colours, upon a lure gules, feathered argent fesswise, a falcon belled or.

MOTTO: 'Vilius virtutibus aurum' – Gold is of less value than virtue.

Arthur Gilstrap Soames was born in 1854, the son of Arthur Soames (1816–94) of Irnham Park, Bourne, Lincolnshire and his wife, Annie Amelia, daughter of Joseph Gilstrap.

He was a Justice of the Peace and a Deputy Lieutenant for the county of Lincoln and High Sheriff in 1903. He was later appointed a Justice of the Peace for Sussex. He married, late in life in 1919, Agnes Helen Van der Heydt, daughter of the Rt. Hon. Sir Robert Peel GCB, PC and widow of D. Van der Heydt. They lived at Sheffield Park, Uckfield, Sussex.

H038a 1899 Arthur G. Soames 9.0 × 6.2 cms

This is an identical plate to H038 except for two heraldic variations. The mallet in base is replaced by two wings conjoined in lure argent and the crest is shown in front of a rising sun proper. The reason for these changes is not known.

H039

H039 1899 Arthur G. Soames 6.0 × 5.2 cms

A small engraved crest plate with helmet and mantling within a decorative border. The motto scroll is over and the name scroll is below. It is signed and dated at right hand end of the motto scroll.

CREST: On a wreath of the colours upon a lure gules, feathered argent fesswise, a falcon belled or.

MOTTO: 'Vilius virtutibus aurum' – Gold is of less value than virtue.

See H038 for biographical details.

H040 1899 Arthur G. Soames 9.6 × 6.0 cms

This is a pen and ink design for a pictorial bookplate featuring five sunflowers, in front of a tree on which is perched an owl. It is initialled 'C.H.99'. It is not known, for certain, if this was ever used as a bookplate as no printed version has, so far, been seen but the list in the *Ex Libris Journal* in 1899 included a pictorial plate for Arthur G. Soames.

See H038 for biographical details.

H041 1899 Hubert M. Wilson 8.8 × 6.6 cms

A full panel armorial within a decorative border with the motto over and the name scroll below. There is a canted shield with three quarter facing helmet and awkwardly slanted crest tilting backwards. The lack of tincture lines for the field means it is not possible to provide a complete blazon. The arms are not listed in *Armorial Families*.

ARMS: A chevron embattled between three mullets argent.

CREST: On a wreath of the colours a talbot's head erased argent.

MOTTO: 'Semper vigilans' – Always watchful.

Hubert M. Wilson was born in 1861. In adult life he was Chairman of a brewery company. With his wife, Frances, he had two children and the family lived in some style at Upper Hall, Ledbury, Herefordshire with nine servants including a butler.

He died on 10 June 1939 at Whitchurch, Shropshire.

H042 1899 James Tarbotton Armstrong 9.2 × 7.0 cms

A fine panel pictorial plate with a portrait medallion, of the owner, bottom right. The central feature is a pair of muscular arms embowed grasping a fructed oak tree on which sits an owl. Vertically, on the right, is the motto 'Vi & armis'. On a name scroll at bottom left are the words 'James Tarbotton Armstrong Hys Boke'. The design is an obvious pun on the owner's name, arm-strong, an older version of the name is Strong-i-the-arm. The plate is signed and dated on the left of the name scroll. This plate was exhibited by Helard at the Ex Libris Society Exhibition in January 1901.

James Tarbotton Armstrong was an interesting character in many ways. Born at Totnes in Devon, he was educated at Taunton and later studied at Glasgow and Bonn Universities. In his working life he was an analytical chemist and inventor. Working with a Swede, Axel Orling, he produced, amongst other things the wireless torpedo.

In private life he was a connoisseur and collector, interested in paintings, prints, arms and armour and porcelain to say nothing of bookplates. He was a Vice-President and Hon. Treasurer of the old Ex Libris Society. In adult life he lived in a large house, Desburga, near High Wycombe in Buckinghamshire. Helard's only other portrait plate is that for Mount Allison Ladies College (H126).

H040

H041

H042

H043

H044

H043 1900 Ethel F. Beckett 7.5 × 5.0 cms

A pictorial plate which occurs in black and brown. In the foreground is a harp, a series of fine leather bound books, without legible titles, and a lamp, presumably the lamp of knowledge. Behind are a variety of flowers including a rose, a lily, a sunflower and the fructed branch of an oak tree. The name scroll, at the bottom, reads 'One of the books of Ethel F. Beckett' a form used with better alliterative effect in the next plate for Lilian Crookes. It is signed and dated to the right of the name scroll.

Nothing is known of the owner of this plate.

H044 1900 Lilian A. Crookes 10.0 × 5.5 cms

A pictorial bookplate designed for Helard's younger sister Lilian. Emerging from a vase is a large spray of lilies, a punning allusion to the owner's name, surrounding a name scroll which reads 'One of the books of Lilian A. Crookes'. Around the vase are classical books with legible titles, Dickens, Shakespeare etc. The plate is signed and dated to the left of the name scroll. The original copper plate was found in the Helard archive.

Lilian Ada Crookes was born in Colchester at 5 St Mary's Terrace East, on 14 August 1874. She was the second child of Septimus Crookes and his wife, Anne. At the age of six she moved with her family to Coalbrookdale, She never married and can be seen in later life in the Helard family photograph (fig. 9).

H045 1900 A. Edmund Fraser 10.8 × 7.4 cms

A full panel armorial with three quarter facing helmet and crest slantwise across it with extended wreath. His badge of rank as a knight of St John suspended from the shield. (As it is not an official British order of knighthood it does not carry the prefix 'Sir'.) Signed and dated in a diamond on the right hand side of the helmet. There are mottoes above and below the achievement. He bears the arms of Fraser of Farraline and Gortuleg, suitably differenced, rematriculated in 1896. This plate occurs in black, brown and process reproduction. It was illustrated in the *Ex Libris Journal* Vol. X, 1900.

ARMS: Quarterly 1 and 4, Azure, on a chevron between three fraisiers argent, as many fleurs-de-lis gules, 2 and 3, Argent, three ancient Scots crowns gules, all within a

H045

H046

bordure of the last (for difference), and, as a knight of St John, on a chief gules a cross argent embellished alternately in each of the principle angles with a lion guardant and a unicorn both passant or.

CREST: On a wreath of the colours a buck's head attired and couped proper gorged with an ancient Scots crown or.

MOTTOES:
1. 'Je suis prest' – I am ready.
2. 'Tout bien ou rien' – The whole good or none.

Alexander Edmund Fraser, born 12 February 1863, was the eldest son of John Fraser of Stratherrick (1820–85) and his wife, Susan, daughter of General Thomas Webster of Balgarvie.

He was educated at Oxford, called to the Bar by the Inner Temple and became a diplomat. He was attached to various Embassies in Vienna, Rome, Stockholm, Brussels, Cairo and Washington. He acted as Her Majesty's Agent in the Transvaal from June 1898 till March 1899. He was a Member of the King's Bodyguard of Archers in Scotland.

H046 1900 Graeme Harrison 10.3 × 6.7 cms

A fine full panel armorial plate with canted shield and traditionally facing helmet and crest. The motto is above and name scroll is below. It is signed and dated in the bottom right hand corner. The plate is illustrated in the fifth edition of *Armorial Families*. It occurs in black and dark brown.

ARMS: Or, three piles sable each charged with a demi lion erased of the field holding in the paws a rose gules, on a chief of the second a rose between two escallops of the field.

CREST: On a wreath of the colours, on an escallop between two roses of the last, barbed and seeded proper, a dove or.

MOTTO: 'Vincit virtus omnia' – Virtue conquers all.

Graeme Harrison was born 27 October 1868 the sixth son of Peyton Harrison of Clifton, Albemarle County, Virginia.

He married, 19 March 1888, Alice, daughter of George Ogston and widow of F.A. Marquand. They had two sons and a daughter and lived at Easthorpe House, Ruddington, Nottinghamshire.

H047 1900 Thomas Leadbetter 6.8 × 5.0 cms

A small full panel armorial plate with a canted shield and traditionally facing helmet and crest with the motto over in the Scottish manner. The name scroll is at the bottom. It is signed and dated at the right hand side of the motto scroll. The plate occurs in black and brown.

ARMS: Or, a chevron gules, between two inescutcheons vert in chief and a thistle proper in base, an annulet, for difference, in centre chief. As he was the eldest son it is not clear why the cadency mark for a fifth son should be shown. It is removed from his later plate (H066).

CREST: Out of a mural coronet gules, a demi unicorn ermine, armed, crined and unguled or.

MOTTO: 'Tuta timens' – Fearing safe things.

Thomas Leadbetter was born 21 October 1859 the eldest son of James Greenshields Leadbetter JP (1827–97) of Stobieside, Lanarkshire and his wife, Margaret, only daughter of Hugh Macpherson of Blantyreferme, Lanarkshire. He assumed, by the authority of Lyon King of Arms, in 1902 the additional surname of Greenshields and had a further bookplate made (see H066).

He trained as an architect and entered private practice in 1885. He was a Justice of the Peace and Commissioner of Supply for Lanark, a Fellow of the Society of Antiquaries of Scotland and a Member of the Royal Company of Archers (The Monarch's Bodyguard for Scotland). He inherited Stobieside, Strathavon, North Berwick from his father in 1897. He also bought Spittal Tower, Hawick sometime later and restored it.

He married, 1890, Mary Anne, second daughter of Sir John Usher Bart, 1st baronet of Norton and Wells. They had three sons and two daughters. He died on 12 February 1931

H047

H048 1900 Grace Neville 10.8 × 7.7 cms

A fine panel armorial for a maiden lady. The arms in a scrolled lozenge suspended from a ribbon with a guitar to the left and a small dog to the right. Above is a vignette of Glastonbury Tor, Somerset, surrounded by the phrase 'Whatsoever things are lovely think on those things' with a Tudor rose and a portcullis, to left and right (badges of the Neville family). In base, a name scroll 'Grace Neville, Orchard Neville, Co. of Somerset.' The whole surrounded by a gadrooned border. Signed at right hand end of name scroll.

H048

ARMS: Quarterly 1 and 4, Sable, a griffin rampant argent (Griffin), 2 and 3, Quarterley 1 and 4, Gules, on a saltire argent a rose of the field (Neville), 2 and 3, Or, a fretty gules, on a canton of the first a lymphad sable.

Grace Neville was born in 1853. Her father, born in 1818, was the Reverend William Fredrick Neville who married Fanny Blackwood in 1847. The family is related to the Braybrookes of Audley End House, Essex.

Sir John Griffin Griffin was created the 1st Baron Braybrooke in 1788 with special remainder to his cousin Henry Neville who succeeded him as the 2nd Baron Braybrooke. One of Henry's sons, the Hon. George Neville was the Reverend William's father.

H049

H049 1900 A. Charles Pirie 8.0 × 6.0 cms

An etched, seal type, full armorial within a panel, with a small canted shield. It is signed and dated in a small scroll to the bottom right of the panel.

ARMS: Or, a boar's head sable between three pears slipped vert, within a bordure gules.

CREST: On a wreath of the colours, a fawn's head with the sprig of a pear tree in its mouth, proper.

MOTTO: 'Virtute non astutia' – By bravery, not stratagem.

Alexander Charles Pirie was the eldest son of Alexander Pirie of Waterton, Aberdeenshire and his wife, Charlotte Anne, daughter of Colonel Martin Lindsay CB. He lived at Dunecht, Aberdeen.

H050 1900 William Ridley Richardson 11.3 × 6.2 cms

An engraved, full panel armorial, nicely designed with the exception of the shield. Over-use of shading with lack of tincture lines makes the blazon difficult to interpret. Signed and dated to right of name panel. The plate occurs in black and dark brown and was engraved by Downey.

ARMS: Sable, two hawks belled or, on a chief indented ermine, a pale ermines and three lions heads erased, counterchanged (Richardson), impaling, Quarterly 1 and 4, Argent, a saltire engrailed between two escallops in fess gules, on a chief azure an escallop of the field (Tweedy), 2 and 3, Gules, on a bend flory and counterflory between two increscents argent, three lions heads erased sable (Fellowes).

CREST: On a wreath of the colours, upon a mount vert and

H050

in front of a tilting spear fessways, a dexter arm embowed in armour proper, encircled by an annulet or, the hand grasping a sword by the blade in bend sinister proper, pommel and hilt gold, pendent from the wrist by a riband gules, an escutcheon argent charged with a hawk proper.

MOTTO: 'Ben ti voglio' – I wish you well.

William Ridley Richardson MA Cantab was born on 29 October 1856, the only surviving son of John Richardson of Ravensfell and Bromley House in Kent and his wife, Elizabeth, fourth daughter of William Ridley of Felsted, Essex.

He married, 29 April 1886, Elizabeth Harriet, youngest daughter of John Newman Tweedy of Widmore House, Bromley, Kent. They had three sons and three daughters. He inherited Ravensfell and Bromley House, both in Kent which became their family homes.

H051 1900 Sir Thomas Sutherland 7.4 × 5.2 cms

A fine, well balanced engraved full panel armorial with the owner's collar and badge of his knighthood displayed at the bottom. The name scroll enfolding the base, signed and dated along the bottom of the panel. It occurs in black and dark brown.

ARMS: Or, a fess wavy azure issuant therefrom a sun in splendour or between two mullets in chief and a fleur-de-lis in base of the second.

As a Knight Grand Cross of the order of St Michael and St George he was granted supporters which are not shown. To the dexter, a sailor holding in his dexter hand a lead line, all proper, and to the sinister, a Lascar seaman holding in the dexter hand a flagstaff with a banner azure charged with a rudder in bend sinister surmounted by an anchor or. The sinister hand, in each case, is supporting the shield.

CREST: On a wreath of the colours, a cat salient, holding in its mouth a thistle leaved and slipped proper, between two roses gules leaved and stalked vert.

MOTTO: 'Auspicium melioris avi' – The token of a better age.

Thomas Sutherland was born in 1834, the only son of Robert Sutherland of Aberdeen and his wife, Christian, daughter of Thomas Webster. He was educated at Aberdeen University and was, for thirty-four years chairman of the Peninsular and Oriental Steam Navigation Co. and a director and vice-chairman of the Suez Canal Co. He was the founder and first chairman of the Hong Kong and Shanghai Banking Corporation. He served as MP for Greenock from 1884–1900. He was created Knight Commander of the Most Distinguished Order of St Michael and St George (KCMG) in 1891 and Knight Grand Cross of the same order (GCMG) in 1897.

He married, in 1880, Alice, daughter of the Reverend John Macnaught, vicar of St Chrysostom's in Liverpool.

H051

H052 1900 Marcia, Countess of Yarborough

8.7 × 7.0 cms

This is one of Helard's best plates, for a Countess who is also a peeress in her own right, showing arms, quarterly of eight, in a lozenge with supporters beneath her coronet of rank as a baroness. Unusually for a panel plate of this quality it is neither signed nor dated. It is only known printed in brown.

ARMS: Quarterly of eight, 1, Argent, a chevron between three foxes heads erased gules (Fox), 2, Argent, a lion rampant gules within a bordure sable, on a canton azure a harp or (Lane), 3, Quarterly ermine and azure, a cross or (Osborne), 4, Azure, three cinquefoils, two and one between nine cross crosslets, three, three and three argent (Darcy), 5, Azure, three bars gemelles and a chief or (Meynell), 6, Azure, a maunch or (Conyers), 7, Gules, on a saltire argent a fleur-de-lis azure (Nevill), 8, Because of the angle of the lozenge and the paw of the sinister supporter obscuring part of the design it has not been possible to identify this coat.

SUPPORTERS: On either side a lion rampant azure.

Marcia Amelia Mary Lane-Fox was born on 18 October 1863 the eldest daughter and heir of the 12th Baron Conyers. She succeeded to her father's title in 1892. As this was a Barony by Writ it could be transmitted in the female line in the absence of heirs male.

She married, in 1886, Charles Alfred Worsley Pelham PC 4th Earl of Yarborough. They had three sons, the eldest Charles, born 1887, was killed in action 1914.

The barony of Fauconberg had been in abeyance since 1463. In 1903 the abeyance was terminated in her favour so as well as being Countess of Yarborough she was Baroness Fauconberg and Conyers in her own right. The case was prepared and presented to the House of Lords by Arthur Charles Fox-Davies.

These titles passed to her eldest surviving son, the 5th Earl of Yarborough but became abeyant again after his death. She was Commandant of the Brocklesby Park Auxiliary Hospital during the 1914–18 War and became an Officer of the Most Excellent Order of the British Empire (OBE) in 1920. She and her husband were guests at Helard's wedding. The Lane-Foxes are related to John Fox, Charles Fox-Davies's grandfather.

H052

H053 1901 John M. Knapp 9.5 × 6.6 cms

An engraved full panel armorial plate with a canted impaled shield. Signed and dated at the end of the motto scroll. This plate is only known printed in brown.

ARMS: Per pale or and sable, a lion passant counterchanged, holding in the dexter paw a broken sword in bend sinister blade downwards proper, pommel and hilt gold, on a chief dancettee per pale of the second and of the first, three helmets of the third garnished gold (Knapp), impaling, Argent, a lion rampant sable grasping in the dexter paw a sword, pommel and hilt or, the blade entwined by a serpent proper, between three crescents gules (Brownrigg).

CREST: On a wreath of the colours, upon a laurel branch vert, an arm embowed in armour proper, garnished gold grasping a broken sword as in the arms.

MOTTO: 'In bello aut in pace' – In war or peace.

John Matthew Knapp was born on 3 April 1868, the eldest son of Matthew Knapp JP, DL and his wife, Catherine, daughter of Lieutenant Robert Robertson Bruce, Bengal Horse Artillery. He was educated at Magdalen College, Oxford (MA) and was a Justice of the Peace for Buckinghamshire.

He married, 20 June 1900, Katherine Laura, only child of the Reverend John Studholme Brownrigg, Canon of Bangor. They lived at Linford Hall, Wolverton, Bucks.

H054 1901 Richard Southcote Mansergh
5.8 × 7.0 cms

A nicely designed oblong panel armorial engraved by Downey. Signed and dated at the beginning of motto scroll. The plate occurs in black and dark brown.

ARMS: Argent, a bend raguly gules between three arrows, points downwards of the last, flighted and barbed or.

CREST: Out of a ducal coronet proper, charged with a label of three points gules, a demi lion rampant argent, gorged with a collar raguly of the second and holding in the dexter paw an arrow point downwards of the last, flighted and barbed or.

MOTTO: 'Tout jour prêt' – Always ready.

Richard Southcote Mansergh was born on 25 October 1859, the eldest son of Richard St George Mansergh of Friarsfield, Tipperary and his wife, Sophia Elizabeth, eldest daughter of Richard Oliver Ellard of Newton Ellard, Co. Limerick. He was the brother of Charlotte Mansergh (H055). He inherited his uncle's estate, Grenane, Co. Tipperary in 1899. He was a Justice of the Peace for the county.

He had a number of bookplates to his name besides this one, including one by C.W. Sherborn and another by George Eve (see fig. 14).

H055 1901 Charlotte R. Mansergh 7.3 × 5.0 cms

An engraved panel armorial with the arms in a lozenge for a maiden lady, the engraving is by Downey. It is signed at right hand end of the name scroll and dated in the right margin.

ARMS: Argent, a bend raguly gules between three arrows, point downwards of the last, flighted and barbed or.

MOTTO: 'Tout jour prêt' – Always ready.

Charlotte Mansergh was the daughter of Richard St George Mansergh of Friarsfield, Co. Tipperary and his wife, Sophia Elizabeth, daughter of Richard Ellard, and sister of Richard Southcote Mansergh (H054).

H055

H056 1901 Harry North 10.8 × 6.6 cms

A panel armorial with impaled coat, motto above and name scroll below. Signed and dated at the bottom right. The shield is canted with the helmet awkwardly draped over the corner and the wreath balanced precariously on top. This plate, which was engraved by Downey, is illustrated in *Armorial Families* fifth edition (1905) (see also H127).

ARMS: Argent, two chevronels nebuly between two mullets in chief and a decrescent in base sable (North), impaling, Or, a dragon sable, in chief three roses gules slipped and leaved proper and in base a fleur-de-lis also gules (Evans).

CREST: On a wreath of the colours a lion's head erased argent, gorged with a collar nebuly between two mullets all sable.

MOTTO: 'Animo et fide' – With resolution and fidelity.

Sir Harry North was the son of John Thomas North of Avery Hill, Eltham, Kent, who died in 1896, and his wife Jane, second daughter of John Woodhead of Leeds, Yorkshire. He was born on 26 December 1866 and educated at Jesus College, Cambridge.

He was a Captain and Honorary Major in the 4th Battalion Royal Munster Fusiliers. He retired in 1905 and was knighted the same year. He was one of His Majesty's Lieutenants for the City of London.

He married, 5 December 1894, Jessica Louisa second daughter of David Evans JP of Cliffden, Saltburn, Middlesburgh (H065) and had one son and one daughter. He lived at Lemonswell, Eltham, Kent and died 26 November 1920.

H056

H057 1901 Francis Oppenheimer 9.2 × 6.0 cms

A fine engraved, full panel armorial, using tincture lines, with a canted shield and totally unrealistic crest, if one thinks of it on top of the helmet during a joust. This is the fault of the Kings of Arms who made the Grant, not the bookplate designer. This plate was made before the granting of his two knighthoods. It is signed and dated at the top of the 'Ex libris' scroll.

ARMS: Quarterly, gules and azure, a cross invected between a lion rampant, regardant, supporting a flagstaff therefrom flowing, to the dexter, a banner in the first and fourth quarters and in the second and third, an anchor erect all or.

CREST: On a wreath of the colours, two branches of oak in saltire vert fructed or, in front of a flagstaff in bend proper, therefrom flowing a banner gules , surmounting a trident in bend sinister also proper.

MOTTO: 'Nihil sine labore' – Nothing without labour.

Francis Charles Oppenheimer was born on 17 December 1870, the eldest son of Sir Charles Oppenheimer Kt, Consul General for the Grand Duchies of Hess and of Baden and his wife, Bertha, daughter of Leopold Goldbeck of Frankfurt-on-Main.

He was educated at Balliol College, Oxford, called to the Bar by The Middle Temple and was appointed HM Consul General for the City of Frankfurt, Province of Hesse, Nassau and the Grand Duchy of Hesse 1900–12. Commercial Attaché to British Embassy at Berlin and Legations at The Hague, Copenhagen and Stockholm 1912–20. He was knighted (Knight Bachelor) in 1907 and made a Knight Commander of the Most Distinguished Order of St Michael and St George (KCMG) in 1915.

H057

H058

H058 1901 Thornycroft 9.8 × 6.3 cms

A full panel armorial plate with the single name 'Thornycroft' in the name scroll at the base. It is signed and dated at the end of the name scroll. This is illustrated in *Armorial Families* fifth edition and is most likely to be the plate of John Edward Thornycroft eldest son of Sir John Isaac Thornycroft Kt, FRS, LLD. The arms shown are those of a gentleman whereas John Isaac was knighted by this time and John Edward was not knighted until 1918.

ARMS: Per pale vert and azure, four mascules interlaced in fess or between four cross crosslets argent, two and two.

CREST: On a wreath of the colours, upon the battlements of a tower gules , a falcon rising proper, belled and jessed or, the whole between two branches of a thorn tree or.

MOTTO: 'Fortis qui se vincit' – Brave is he who conquers himself.

John Isaac Thornycroft was born in 1843 in Rome, the eldest son of Thomas Thornycroft of Gawsworth, Cheshire, and his wife, Mary, second daughter of John Francis of Thornham.

He married, in 1871, Blanche Ada, second daughter of Frederick Coules of Gloucester. They had two sons and five daughters and the family homes were at Steyne, Isle of Wight and Eyot Villa, Chiswick, London.

He worked at Palmer's Ship Building and Iron Co. before studying engineering in Glasgow under Lord Kelvin. He built his first steam launch at the age of nineteen and then established a ship building yard on the Thames at Chiswick in 1864. He built his first ship for the Royal Navy, a steam torpedo boat, in 1877. He later moved into the manufacture of steam powered road vehicles. The company was taken over by Vickers in 1960. He died at his family home on the Isle of Wight in 1928.

His son, John Edward was born in 1872 and married, 1896, Isabel only daughter of Albert Ward JP. He continued his father's steam engine business and was created a Knight of the Most Excellent Order of the British Empire (KBE) in 1918. He lived at Bembridge, Isle of Wight and at The Clock House, Chiswick, London.

H059 1901 William Henry Watts 7.0 × 5.3 cms

A full panel armorial with typical Helard mantling and the crest balanced precariously on a slightly bent wreath extending far beyond the crown of the helmet. Signed and dated at the bottom right. The plate occurs in black and dark brown.

ARMS: Gules, a lion rampant argent, holding in the mouth a sprig of oak leaved fructed and slipped proper, in chief two portcullises or.

CREST: On a wreath of the colours a greyhound sejant or gorged with a collar gemmel azure, holding in the mouth a sprig of oak as in the arms and resting the dexter foreleg on an antique shield of the second charged with a portcullis of the first.

MOTTO: 'Labore gaudeo' – I rejoice in labour.

William Henry Watts was born on 8 February 1851 the eldest son of William Henry Watts JP, Lord Mayor of Liverpool 1894/5 and his wife Harriet, daughter of William Suter and the grandson of the Reverend Isaac Watts. He had three brothers and four sisters. The family home was Elm Hall, Wavertree, Liverpool.

H059

H060 1902 Henry J.B. Clements
6.6 cms diameter (excluding name scroll)

This is one of the plates given away to selected readers of the *Genealogical Magazine*, produced from half tone block and limited to one-hundred copies. This one was for September 1902 it is signed to right of name scroll. The lack of tincture lines makes it impossible to blazon the arms from the bookplate.

ARMS: Argent, two bends wavy sable, on a chief gules three besants (Clements), on an escutcheon of pretence, Ermine, on a bordure engrailed gules eight mullets or (Wickham).

CREST: On a wreath of the colours, a hawk close and belled proper.

MOTTO: 'Patriis virtutibus' – With his father's virtues.

Henry John Beresford Clements was born on 22 October 1869, the eldest son of Henry Theophilus Clements JP, DL for the county of Cavan, Ireland and his wife, Gertrude Caroline Lucy, the daughter of the Reverend David Markham, rector of Great Horkesley, Essex and Canon of Windsor.

He married 31 October 1893, Eleonore, the younger daughter, and co-heir, of William Wickham MP and they had three sons and three daughters.

He was a Justice of the Peace for the county of Kildare, Deputy Lieutenant for the county of Leitrim and Sheriff for the same county in 1893.

H060

H061 1902 Sydney M. Collins 6.9 × 6.3 cms

This is a panel armorial, screen printed from a block. It was a presentation to the owner in December 1902 by the *Genealogical Magazine* and limited to one-hundred copies. Initialled under the right hand cartouche and dated under the left. The cartouches each depict a pelican in her piety. The lack of tincture lines makes blazoning difficult. There are a number of families of this name listed in *Armorial Families* none of whom use this form of the arms.

ARMS: ?, on a bend ? argent three martlets sable.

CREST: A demi griffin collared.

MOTTO: 'Colens deum et regem' – Worshipping God and the King.

Nothing is known about the owner. The arms are not listed in *Armorial Families*.

H061

H062

H063

H062 1902 John George Crozier 8.7 × 4.3 cms

This is another plate, presented in July 1902 by the *Genealogical Magazine*, produced from a half tone block and limited to one-hundred copies. It is signed and dated at the right hand end of the name scroll.

ARMS: Or, on a cross between four fleur-de-lis azure a crozier of the field.

CREST: On a wreath of the colours, a demi eagle displayed proper, charged on the breast with a cross patee or.

MOTTO: 'Vi et virtute' – By strength and valour.

John George Crozier was born on 22 April 1869, the only son of John Crozier JP of Gortra House, Co. Fermanagh and his wife, Anne, the daughter of James Tymons. He became a Justice of the Peace for Co. Fermanagh and was High Sheriff in 1897.

He married on 4 August 1891, Marian Georgiana, the eldest daughter of Lucan Bingham, Inspector in the Royal Irish Constabulary. They had one son, John Spencer Noel and one daughter, Helena Inez. On the death of his father the family lived at Gortra House, Co. Fermanagh.

H063 1902 Rev. F.B. Dickinson 8.5 × 9.5 cms

This is another presentation plate made, in January 1902, by the *Genealogical Magazine*. It is produced from a half tone block, limited to one-hundred copies and signed bottom right. The canted shield is to the left with motto over with the helmet, crest and mantling to the right. The lack of tincture lines makes it impossible to blazon the arms accurately. They are not listed in *Armorial Families* which is surprising. Fox-Davies was editor of the Magazine. Why would he select someone who did not apparently bear arms lawfully to receive free copies of an armorial plate? The original drawing for the shield is in the Helard archive.

ARMS: A fess ermine between two lions passant.

CREST: on a wreath of the colours a demi lion.

MOTTO: 'Praemium virtutis honor' – Honour is the reward of virtue.

Frederick Brinley Dickinson was born in 1833. He graduated BA from Brasenose College, Oxford in 1855. He was ordained by the Bishop of Worcester in 1857 and raised to the priesthood by the Bishop of Exeter in 1858. He served as curate in various parishes including St Martin-in-the-Fields, London before being appointed vicar of Ashford in Middlesex 1872–87. He spent his later years at The Manor House, Ottery St Mary, Devon.

He died there aged seventy-one in 1904.

H064

H065

H064 1902 Walter F. Dunsterville 11.3 × 8.0 cms

Again this plate was presented, in November 1902 by the *Genealogical Magazine*, printed from a half tone block and limited to one-hundred copies. Lack of tincture lines again causes difficulty with the blazon. Full achievement on a pargetted background and signed bottom right.

ARMS: ? fretty ?, on a canton a lion passant.

CREST: On a wreath of the colours a demi lion?

MOTTO: 'Auspicio coeli' – With a token of heaven.

Walter Frerichs Dunsterville was born in August 1865 the son of Colonel James Barnes Dunsterville (1821–87) and his wife Harriet daughter of Captain George Birch. He was educated at Wellington College and for many years he was involved with the pearl trade in the Persian Gulf.

He married, on 7 June 1894 in London, Gwynedd Maud Vallings and in 1901 the family were living at 34 Rossetti Mansions, Chelsea. He died in 1943.

H065 1902 David Evans 8.6 × 5.9 cms

A full panel armorial with three quarter helmet but the crest facing left slantwise across the helmet balanced precariously on an extended, slightly bent wreath. The motto is above and the name scroll below. It is signed and dated at the left hand of the motto scroll. The plate is known in black and brown.

ARMS: Or, a dragon sable, in chief three roses gules slipped and leaved proper and in base a fleur-de-lis also gules.

CREST: On a wreath of the colours, in front of a javelin erect proper, a dragon statant sable holding in the mouth a rose as in the arms.

MOTTO: 'Y dewraf ennilla' – The bravest man will win.

David Evans was born in October 1841, the son of Evan Evans of Trecynon, Aberdare, Glamorgan and his wife, Rachel, nee Hopkins.

He married, in June 1864, Jane, daughter of David Thomas of Llantwit Major, Cowbridge. They had two sons and two daughters. The younger daughter, Jessie Louisa, married Major Harry North (H056). The family home was Cliffden, Saltburn, Middlesburgh.

H065a 1902 David Evans 8.6 × 5.9 cms

An almost identical plate but this time etched and printed in brown. The result is a design which is by no means as clear as the engraved plate. The etching would have been done by Helard.

H066 1902 Greenshields-Leadbetter 13.3 × 8.2 cms

A fine large engraved full panel armorial with impaled shield and typical Helard mantling. The motto is above and the name scroll below. It is signed and dated bottom right (see also H047).

ARMS: Or, a chevron gules, between two inescutcheons vert in chief and a thistle proper in base (Leadbetter), impaling, Gules, a saltire between four batons argent garnished sable (Usher).

CREST: Out of a mural coronet gules, a demi unicorn ermine, armed, crined and unguled or.

MOTTO: 'Tuta timens' – Fearing safe things.

Thomas Leadbetter, born 21 October 1859, the eldest son of James Greenshields Leadbetter of Stobieside. He took the additional surname Leadbetter by the authority of Lord Lyon King of Arms in 1902 and this plate probably celebrates that event. He trained as an architect and commenced practice in 1885. He was a Justice of the Peace and Commissioner of Supply for Lanark and a Member of the Royal Company of Archers (The Monarch's Bodyguard for Scotland).

He married, 1890, Mary Anne, second daughter of Sir John Usher Bart. of Norton and Wells. They had three sons and two daughters and lived at Stobieside, Strathavon, North Berwick and Spittal Tower, Hawick.

H066a 1902 Greenshields-Leadbetter 7.0 × 4.0 cms

Identical plate to the above but much smaller.

H067 1902 **The Earl of Mar and Kellie** 7.0 × 4.5 cms

A small armorial plate produced from a half tone block depicting a quartered shield beneath an earl's coronet. The name scroll is below, It is indistinctly signed bottom right. This is one of the plates produced for selected subscribers of the *Genealogical Magazine* and presented in June 1902 (see Section II). It is not an inspired production.

ARMS: Quarterly, 1 and 4, Argent, a pale sable (Erskine), 2 and 3, Azure, a bend between six cross crosslets fitchee (Mar), overall on an escutcheon gules, the Royal Crown of Scotland proper within a double tressure flory counterflory or, ensigned with an earl's coronet (Kellie).

Walter John Francis Erskine KT 12th Earl of Mar and 14th Earl of Kellie, and, as Viscount Fentham, premier viscount of Scotland was born on 29 August 1865 and succeeded to the titles in 1888.

He was educated at Eton, formerly a lieutenant in the Scots Guards and Hon. Lieutenant Colonel, Argyll and Sutherland Highlanders. He was Lord Lieutenant of Clackmannanshire, and a Lieutenant in the Royal Company of Archers, the King's Bodyguard in Scotland. He was appointed Hereditary Keeper of Stirling Castle, with remainder to heirs male, in 1923.

He married, 1892, Lady Susan Violet Ashley, daughter of the 8th Earl of Shaftsbury and had one son, John Francis Ashley, Lord Erskine, born 26 April 1895.

The family estates were Alloa House, Clackmannanshire and Kellie Castle, in Fife.

H067

H068

H068 1902 **Gery Milner-Gibson-Cullum**
6.9 × 5.2 cms

A full panel armorial with quartered coat and twin crests with motto above and name scroll below. Signed and dated at far right end of name scroll. The plate occurs in black, shades of brown and, unusually, in red.

ARMS: Quarterly, 1 and 4, Azure, a chevron ermine between three pelicans or vulning themselves proper (Cullum), 2 and 3, Azure, three bridle-bits chevronways between as many storks close argent (Milner).

CRESTS:
1. On a wreath of the colours a lion sejant or, holding between the paws a column argent, the capital and base or (Cullum).
2. On a wreath of the colours, a stork close argent, holding in the beak a branch of laurel proper, resting the dexter foot on a bridle-bit or (Milner).

MOTTO: 'Sustineatur' – Let him be sustained (Cullum).

George Gery Milner-Gibson was born in 1857, the fifth but only surviving son of the Rt. Hon. Thomas Milner-Gibson MP of Theberton House, Suffolk and his wife, Arethusa Susanna, only child and heir of the Reverend Sir Thomas Gery Cullum, eighth and last baronet, of Hardwick House, Bury St Edmonds, Suffolk and his wife, Mary Anne, only child of Henry Eggers of Woodford, Essex.

H068a

CREST: On a wreath of the colours, a triple towered castle sable masoned argent, from the central tower a flag flying of the last charged with a cross gules.

MOTTO: 'Patience and resolution'.

James Mitchell Mutter was born on 8 April 1845 the eldest son of James Mutter JP, of Bowmore, Islay, Argyllshire and his wife, Agnes, only child of George Cruickshanks of Glasgow. He was a Justice of the Peace for the county of Argyll and one time major in the Argyll and Bute Artillery.

He married, 6 August 1873, Isabella, daughter of Alexander Morrison, a merchant in Glasgow. They had three sons and one daughter. He emigrated to British Columbia and was a member of the Legislative Assembly for the District of Cowiehan-Alberni. The family lived at Somenosdale, Somenos, British Columbia, having previously lived at Bunanuisg, Isle of Islay, Argyllshire.

He was educated at Trinity College, Cambridge and became a Justice of the Peace and Deputy Lieutenant for Suffolk and High Sheriff in 1888.

He inherited Hardwick House in 1875 on the death of his grandmother, Lady Cullum, whose name he assumed by Royal Licence 9 December 1878. He was Hon. Curator of the Moyses Museum, Bury St. Edmonds, 1912 and Mayor of the same town in 1913–14 having previously been made an Honorary Freeman in 1911. He was a Fellow of the Society of Antiquaries and a Fellow of the Zoological Society of London. He contributed numerous articles to genealogical and archaeological publications. He died on 21 November 1921. Hardwick House was demolished in the 1970s and is now the site of the West Suffolk Hospital.

H068a 1902 Gery Milner-Gibson-Cullum

4.9 × 3.8 cms

This is an engraved full panel armorial of a slightly different design and is the smallest plate Helard produced. It occurs in three shades of brown and a process reproduction in black.

H069 1902 James Mitchell Mutter 10.0 × 6.4 cms

This is a half tone block print, one of the ones given away free to selected readers of the *Genealogical Magazine* this one in August 1902. Full panel armorial without the use of tincture lines, initialled 'C.H.' bottom left.

ARMS: Gules, on a fess between three escutcheons or , a boar's head couped between two mascules of the first.

H069

H070

H070 1902 Grace Neville 8.0 cms diameter

A circular seal-type armorial for a maiden lady, arms in a lozenge surmounted by the portcullis badge of the Nevilles. Arms surrounded by sprigs of roses. Name on scroll above and on a scroll below 'Ex Libris May 1902'. This example is a signed proof on card.

ARMS: Gules, on a saltire cross argent a rose of the field.

For further details of the owner see H048.

H071 1903 Sir Jonathan Edmund Backhouse Bart.
4.3 × 10.0 cms

A large full panel armorial plate for a baronet with the motto above and the name scroll below. Signed and dated, outside the panel, bottom right. A total lack of tincture lines together with some slight inaccuracies in the blazon render the plate armorially inadequate but this does not detract from the decorative effect as a whole. The plate occurs in black and dark brown and was engraved by Downey.

ARMS: Quarterly, 1 and 4, Party per saltire or and azure, a saltire engrailed ermine between two roses in pale gules, barbed and seeded proper and as many passion crosses in fess of the first (Backhouse), 2 and 3, Ermine, on a chevron azure three foxes heads erased within a bordure flory of the second, on a canton of the same a drinking cup of the third surmounted by three fleur-de-lis argent (Fox), his badge of rank as a baronet in the centre point, impaling, Quarterly, 1 and 4, Argent, a chevron sable between three oak leaves slipped proper, 2 and 3, Gules, a lion rampant per bend sinister argent and erminois,

H071a

H071

ducally crowned or between three crescents, on a canton of the last, a bear's head erased muzzled sable (Salusbury-Trelawny).

CREST: On a wreath of the colours, in front of a rock proper, thereon an eagle displayed vert, holding in each claw a passion cross or, a serpent on its back, the tail nowed proper.

MOTTO: 'Confido in Deo' – I trust in God.

The Backhouses were a banking family in the North East of England. Jonathan Backhouse (1779–1842), Sir Jonathan's grandfather, was a third generation banker from Darlington. He helped to raise the finance for the Stockton and Darlington Railway. His son, Edmund, was Member of Parliament for Darlington and also a banker. The

Backhouse Bank was ultimately subsumed into Barclays Bank Ltd.

Jonathan Edmund Backhouse was born on 15 November 1849 the elder son of Edmund Backhouse and his wife, Juliet Mary, only child and heiress of Charles Fox of Trebah, hence the heraldic quartering. He had a twin brother, Roger, who grew up to become Admiral Sir Roger Backhouse (1878–1942). Jonathan was educated at Rugby and Trinity Hall, Cambridge. He was a Justice of the Peace and Deputy Lieutenant for the North Riding of Yorkshire and Deputy Lieutenant for the county of Durham. He was created a baronet in 1901.

He married, 29 November 1871, Florence, youngest child of Sir John Salusbury-Trelawny, 9th baronet.

He lived at Uplands, Darlington, County Durham and died 27 July 1918. He was succeeded, as 2nd baronet, by his son Edmund Trelawny Backhouse.

H071a 1903 Sir Jonathan Edmund Backhouse
8.5 × 5.8 cms

A similar plate to the above but much smaller, signed and dated 1903. It occurs in two states, one with identical lettering and one with the name scroll altered to read only, 'E.Libris Sir Jonathan Edmund Backhouse Baronet'.

H072 1903 Sir Maurice C. Boileau Bart. 12.4 × 7.6 cms

A circular armorial design with superimposed crest, this is one of the plates made for selected readers of *The Genealogical Magazine*, this one in February 1903, and produced, in a hundred copies, from a half tone block (see Section III). The lack of tincture lines makes deciphering the quarterings difficult, Fox-Davies only cites the pronomial quarter in his description and does not have the crest arising out of a ducal crown. Signed and dated at right hand end of name scroll.

ARMS: Quarterly, 1 and 4, Azure, a triple towered castle and in base a crescent or (Boileau), 2 and 3, On a bend cottised between six mascules each charged with an escallop, six escallops. In the centre point his badge of rank as a baronet.

CREST: On a wreath of the colours, a pelican in her piety proper, charged on the breast with a saltire gules. (shown here arising out of a ducal crown).

MOTTO: 'De tout mon Coeur' – With all my heart.

Maurice Colborne Boileau was born on 3 December 1865. He was the third, but eldest surviving son, of Sir Francis

H072

George Manningham Boileau Bart. and his wife, Lucy Henrietta, daughter of Sir George Edward Nugent Bart. He was educated at Worcester College, Oxford and succeeded his father, as 3rd baronet, in 1900. He was a landowner with over four-thousand acres in Norfolk and lived at Ketteringham Park, Wymondham, Norfolk. He died on 13 September 1937 and was succeeded by his brother, Raymond Frederic Boileau, as the 4th baronet.

H073 1904 John Biddulph 9.0 × 6.2 cms

Engraved by Downey, this is a full panel armorial with canted shield, traditional side-facing helmet and crest with well-fitting wreath. The motto above and the name scroll below. It is signed and dated, outside the panel, at bottom right.

Arms: Vert, an eagle displayed argent, armed and langued gules, a canton of the second.

Crest: On a wreath of the colours, a wolf rampant argent, charged on the breast with a trefoil slipped vert.

Motto: 'Sublimiora petamus' – Let us aim at loftier things.

John Biddulph was born on 25 July 1840, the third son of Robert Biddulph, JP and DL, MP for Hereford and his

wife, Elizabeth, daughter of George Palmer MP of Nazeing Park, Essex. He became a Colonel in the Indian Political Service.

He married, 1882, Julia, daughter of Sir John Martin. In England they lived at Grey Court, Ham, Surrey.

H074 1904 Edith Peruzzi de Medici 5.6 × 3.7 cms

A small engraved full panel armorial for a titled lady, signed and dated bottom right. It occurs in black and dark brown and was engraved by Downey.

Arms: The lack of tincture lines makes complete blazoning impossible. The features are, on a pale, between to the dexter six pears slipped in a circle and to the sinister a lion rampant double queued (this charge also features in the arms of Story), five roundels two, two and one, below an oval escutcheon bearing three fleur-de-lis.

Motto: 'Felix conjunctio' – A happy union.

Edith Marion Story was born in 1844 the daughter of William Wetmore Story (1819–95) an American lawyer and later sculptor living in Rome. She was the brother of Julian Russell Story (H086). She was a writer and friend of Elizabeth Barrett Browning. She married Marchese Simone de Peruzzi de Medici, a descendant of an ancient banking family and legal heir to the renowned Medici family. He was Court Chamberlain to King Victor Emmanuel II of Italy and later to King Umberto.

She died in 1907.

H073

H074

H075 1904 Lady Katherine Scott Usher

7.2 × 5.2 cms

This is an engraved panel armorial with impaled shield for a married lady. The shield is suspended from a knotted ribbon and surrounded by foliage, name scroll at bottom. Signed and dated, outside the panel, bottom right and engraved by Downey.

ARMS: Gules, a saltire between four batons argent garnished sable, a canton charged with the badge of rank of a baronet (Usher), impaling, Per chevron argent and sable three bulls heads erased counterchanged (Turnbull).

Katherine Scott Turnbull was the daughter of James Turnbull of Edinburgh. She married, 1890, Robert Usher, born 25 May 1860, who was the eldest son of Sir John Usher Bart. (1899), and his wife, Mary Ann, daughter of Thomas Balmer.

Robert succeeded to his father's baronetcy, as 2nd baronet, in 1904 and this plate probably commemorates that elevation.

H076 1905 Miles R. Backhouse 9.5 × 5.9 cms

An engraved, full panel, armorial plate with canted impaled shield. It occurs in black and dark brown. Signed and dated outside panel at bottom right. It was engraved by Downey.

ARMS: Quarterly, 1 and 4, Party per saltire or and azure, a saltire engrailed ermine between two roses in pale gules, barbed and seeded proper and as many passion crosses in fess of the first (Backhouse), 2 and 3, Ermine, on a chevron azure three foxes heads erased or, within a bordure flory of the second, on a canton of the same a drinking cup, of the third, surmounted by three fleur-de-lis argent (Fox), impaling, Argent, a lion rampant tail elevated between two mullets in fess sable (Buxton).

CREST: On a wreath of the colours, in front of a rock proper, thereon an eagle displayed vert holding , in each claw, a passion cross or, a serpent on its back, the tail nowed proper.

MOTTO: 'Confido in Deo' – I trust in God.

H075

H076

Miles Roland Charles Backhouse was born on 24 November 1878, the fourth son of Sir Jonathan Edmund Backhouse Bart. (H069) and his wife, Florence, daughter of Sir John Trelawny Bart. He was educated at Eton and Trinity Hall, Cambridge. He married, 1904, Olive, daughter of Geoffrey Buxton and they had three sons and a daughter.

He was a professional soldier, served in the 14th Squadron of the Imperial Yeomanry in the Boer War, South Africa, 1900–02 and was awarded the DSO. He served in various regiments during the 1914–18 War, reaching the rank of Lieutenant Colonel, was mentioned in despatches four times and awarded a bar to his DSO in 1917.

He was a director of the La Protetrice Insurance Co. and a director of the Brixton Estates Ltd. He was also President of the International Sleeping Car Company.

He died on 15 May 1962.

H076a Miles R. Backhouse 9.5 × 5.9 cms

Identical plate to the above but etched by Helard herself, in brown. The result is a much softer picture with darker shading.

H077 1905 Lionel Cust 9.5 × 6.8 cms

This is a large engraved plate, full armorial panel with a canted impaled shield. The motto above and the name scroll below. It is signed and dated at the base of the shield. In a letter to Alfred Downey, the engraver (see Section III), Helard, whilst asking for a few alterations, says how pleased both she and her husband are with the outcome of the design.

ARMS: Ermine, on a chevron sable three fountains proper and in centre chief a mullet on a crescent for cadency (Cust), impaling, Argent, a chevron between three escallops sable (Lyttelton).

CREST: On a wreath of the colours a lion's head erased sable gorged with a collar paly wavy of six argent and azure.

MOTTO: 'Qui custodit caveat' – Let he who guards beware.

Lionel Henry Cust was born on 25 January 1859 the son of Sir Reginald Cust, barrister, and his wife, Lady Elizabeth Caroline, eldest daughter of the 5th Earl of Darnley. Educated at Eton and Trinity College, Cambridge he entered the War Office in 1882. He transferred to the British Museum, becoming Assistant Keeper in the Department of Prints and Drawings in 1884. He was Director of the National Portrait Gallery 1895–1909, Surveyor of the King's Pictures and Works of Art 1901–27 and Gentleman Usher to the King 1901–27. He was made a Commander of the Royal Victorian Order (CVO) in 1914 and Knight Commander in the same Order (KCVO) in 1927. He wrote widely on pictures and drawings in the Royal Collection.

He married, 1895, the Hon. Sybil Lyttelton, daughter of the 4th Lord Lyttelton. They had one son, Lionel George, and lived at Datchet House, Datchet near Windsor.

He died 12 October 1929.

H077a 1905 Lionel Cust 5.0 × 3.6 cms

This is an identical plate to the above but in a smaller size. It occurs in black and dark brown, also engraved by Downey.

H077

H078

H078 1905 **Alfred C. Latter** 8.2 × 5.9 cms

A full panel armorial with canted shield and illustrated in Armorial Families fifth edition. Good, well balanced plate signed and dated outside the panel at bottom right and engraved by Downey.

ARMS: Azure, three wedding favours, two and one, bowed argent, on a chief of the last a terrestrial sphere proper.

CREST: Out of a crown vallery or, a greyhound's head argent, collared and chained of the first.

MOTTOES:
1. 'A tot bien estrainz'.
2. 'Pour trois' – For three.

Alfred Charles Latter was born in 1857, the son of William Latter of Lee, Kent and his wife, Clara. He married, 1891, Edith Gertrude, second daughter of Charles Henry Plevins of Woodford House, Thrapstone, Northants. They had two sons and a daughter and lived at Southend Hall, Eltham, Kent.

H079

H079 1905 **Gerald Stuart Lysaght** 10 × 6.7 cms

A full panel armorial with Gaelic inscription on the top, motto below and name scroll at the base. Strong, well balanced design signed and dated bottom right. The plate is known in black and dark brown and was engraved by Downey.

ARMS: Argent, three spears erect proper, on a chief crenelle azure a lion passant guardant between two lozenges or.

CREST: On a wreath of the colours, issuant from clouds a naked arm embowed, the hand grasping a dagger by the point all proper.

MOTTO: 'Auxillium de superis' – Help from above.

Gerald Stuart Lysaght was born in 1869 a younger son of John Lysaght (1832–95) of Hengrave Hall, Suffolk and his wife Ellen, daughter of Sidney Moss RN (John's brother, Thomas, married Ellen's sister, Emily Sophia), (see H080). His grandfather was William Lysaght (1800–38) of Hazelwood, County Cork. Gerald married Nina Beatrice Press, daughter of J.L. Press of Clifton, Bristol. He served as a Justice of the Peace for Somerset and was High Sheriff in 1917. He lived at Hunting Ball Lodge, Blue Anchor, Somerset.

He died 7 February 1951.

H080

H081

H080 1905 Sidney Royse Lysaght 6.3 × 6.6 cms

A square full panel armorial with Gaelic inscription at the top and motto below with 'Ex Libris' name scroll at the base. Signed and dated on the right hand of 'Ex Libris' scroll. On only a few occasions did Helard use 'Ex Libris' on her bookplates. The arms are identical to the previous plate but should show differencing marks as the two men were cousins. The plate occurs in black and brown and was engraved by Downey.

ARMS: Argent, three spear heads erect proper, on a chief crenelle azure a lion passant guardant between two lozenges or.

CREST: On a wreath of the colours, issuant from clouds, a naked arm embowed, the hand grasping a dagger by the point all proper.

MOTTO: 'Auxillium de superis' – Help from above.

Sidney Royse Lysaght was born in 1856 the eldest son of Thomas Lysaght of Mintinna, County Cork and his wife Emily Sophia daughter of Sidney Moss RN. He was the cousin of Gerald, (see H079), and grandson of William Lysaght of Hazelwood, County Cork. He was a poet and author and married Katherine, daughter of J. Clarke of Waddington, Lincolnshire. Latterly he lived in his grandfather's house Hazelwood.

He died 20 August 1941.

H081 1905 Heber Mardon 9.2 × 7.4 cms

A very fine full panel armorial with canted shield, tincture lines are not used. The motto ribbon is top left and name scroll is below. It is signed and dated bottom right hand of name scroll. This is an example of Helard's best work and one with which she was justifiably pleased. It was engraved by Alfred Dyer Downey (see Downey correspondence, Section III). It occurs in black and dark brown.

ARMS: Gules, on a bend cottised argent, between two unicorns heads erased of the second, a pellet between two Cornish choughs proper.

CREST: On a wreath of the colours issuant out of a wreath of roses gules, leaved proper, a unicorn's head as in the arms, charged with a pellet.

MOTTO: ' Probitas verus honos' – Probity is true honour.

Heber Mardon, born 1840, was the son of James Mardon (1808–97) and his wife Mary daughter of John Morris. He married, 1860, Anna Maria daughter of Joseph Hall and had four sons and three daughters. He was a Justice of the Peace for the county of Somerset and lived at Astwick, Dulverton, Somerset.

H082 1905 Ethelwyn Pease 6.2 × 5.0 cms

A fine engraved armorial panel with an impaled shield for a married lady suspended from a knotted ribbon. Sprigs of pea blossom in each top corner taken from the arms. Signed and dated bottom right, it was engraved by Downey.

ARMS: Quarterly, 1 and 4, Per fess azure and gules, a fess nebuly ermine between two lambs passant in chief argent and in base, upon a mount proper a dove rising argent, holding in the beak a pea-stalk, the blossom and pods proper (Pease), 2 and 3, Argent, a cross engrailed sable, impaling, Argent, a wolf's head erased with a mullet in dexter chief for difference (Allix).

Laura Matilda Ethelwyn Allix was the daughter of Charles Peter Allix (1842–1920) and his wife, Laura, daughter of R.L. Bevan of Brixworth Hall, Northants. Her father was Vice-Chairman of the Cambridgeshire Quarter Sessions and Deputy-Chairman of the Ely and Bury St Edmunds Light Railway Co. He promoted the construction of the Cambridge to Mildenhall Railway in 1884.

She married, 1 October 1889, Arthur Francis Pease (later to become 1st baronet), they had one son, Richard Arthur Pease (H131) and two daughters. The family home was at Middleton Lodge, Middleton Tyas, Yorkshire. She died in 1936.

H082

H083 1905 Frederick Thomas Penton 11.3 × 5.9 cms

This is a finely engraved plate by the firm of Downey and the engraving cost £4-5s-0d which was queried by Helard as to why it was more than was usually charged (see Section III). The design, which is a full armorial, is not brilliant. The helmet is a poor affair and the crest appears to be a diseased maniacal lion sitting on a magic carpet and floating with little or no relation to the helmet. Signed and dated bottom right. Prints are known in black and dark brown.

ARMS: Per chevron gules and or, two chevronels counter-changed between in chief two towers argent and in base a lion rampant, double queued azure, impaling, Quarterly 1 and 4, Or, a bend compony azure and argent between two lions rampant gules (Stewart), 2 and 3, a saltire cross on a field, unidentified due to lack of tincture lines.

CREST: On a wreath of the colours, a lion couchant guardant, double queued azure, besantee, collared or and resting the dexter paw on a tower as in the arms.

H083

H084

H085

MOTTO: 'Tutus his virtute tutior' – The safe is safer by this virtue.

Frederick Thomas Penton was born in 1851 the son of Henry Penton JP, of Pentonville (1817–82) and his wife, Eliza Maria, daughter of Major Henry Langley of Brittas Castle, Co. Tipperery.

He was a Justice of the Peace for the counties of Middlesex, Buckinghamshire and London and Deputy Lieutenant for Middlesex. He served as a Captain in the 4th Dragoon Guards and later was Member of Parliament. for Finsbury Central from 1886–92. He was High Sheriff for Buckinghamshire 1886–7.

He married in 1883, Caroline Helen Mary, elder daughter of Alexander John Robert Stewart of Ards, Co. Donegal and his wife, Lady Isabel Toler, daughter of the 2nd Earl of Norbury. They had two sons and two daughters, the family home was at Goring Hall, near Worthing, Sussex.

H084 1905 Winfred Porter Truesdell 8.8 × 6.8 cms

An engraved, full panel, armorial with name scroll at base and typical Helard trilobed mantling. Signed and dated outside the panel at bottom right.

ARMS: Argent, upon three piles in chief sable a fess gules, a canton ermines in dexter chief.

CREST: On a wreath of the colours a boar's head erased in pale.

Winfred Porter Truesdell was an American living in Malden, Massachusetts. He was a collector of bookplates and began his collection in 1901 eventually amassing over five-thousand plates. He specialised in children's plates. He had an earlier bookplate made for him by J. Winfred Spenceley in 1902. He was a member of the Ex Libris Society.

H085 1906 Helen Mary Jenkins 5.4 cms diameter

A circular engraved armorial pictorial plate. The arms, for a maiden lady, in a lozenge suspended from a knotted ribbon and surrounded by lilies. The ribbon, threaded through the lilies, bears the inscription, 'I love to lose myself in other men's minds'. The same phrase is used in the plate for Margaret Kahn (H105). Name panel at base, signed and dated bottom right. It was engraved by Downey and is known in black and brown.

ARMS: Or, a lion rampant regardant vert.

Nothing has been discovered concerning the owner.

H086 1906 Julian Russell Story 5.6 × 3.8 cms

A small engraved full panel armorial without tincture lines. It occurs in black, unsigned and in brown, signed and dated with the lion in the shield more clearly defined.

ARMS: A lion rampant double queued.

CREST: A demi lion rampant double queued.

MOTTO: 'Fabula sed vera' – A story but a true one.

Julian Russell Story was born in 1857 at Walton-on-Thames, the son of William Wetmore Story (1819–95) an American lawyer and later sculptor living in Rome. He was the brother of Edith Marion Story who became the Marchesa De Peruzzi de Medici (H074). He was educated at Eton and Brasenose College, Oxford and spent his holidays with his family in Rome surrounded by the literary and artistic elite of that city. After he graduated in 1879 he studied under the American painter Frank Duveneck and became a successful portrait painter.

He died in 1919.

H087 1906 Astley Terry 6.8 × 4.8 cms

This is an engraved, full panel armorial on a diapered ground. His badge, as a knight of the Order of St John of Jerusalem, is suspended from the shield between the name scroll. Signed and dated bottom right.

ARMS: Argent seme gutte d'eau, on a pile in chief gules a lions head upon a fleur-de-lis and upon a bordure sable eight roses of the first.

CREST: On a wreath of the colours a lions head erased argent within an arch of myrtle.

MOTTO: 'Perseveranti dabitur' – It will be given to the persevering.

Astley Fellowes Terry was born on 12 May 1840 in St Georges Road, Hanover Square, London. He had a career in the army starting as an ensign in the Kings Royal Rifle Corp. He rose through the ranks retiring in 1887 as Hon. Major General. He was made a Knight of Grace of St John of Jerusalem. He served in the South African War in 1879, during the Zulu campaign and took part in the operations in East Griqualand in 1880 being promoted to Lieutenant Colonel in 1881.

In 1864 he married Edith Cory and they had four daughters; by 1901 he was a widower living with his four unmarried daughters and three servants in the family home, in which he was born, in St Georges Road, Hanover Square. He co-authored, with S.M. Milne, the annuals of the Kings Royal Rifle Corp in 1913.

He died on 8 December 1926 at the age of eighty-six.

H088 1909 Frederic Dundas Harford 10.8 × 6.2 cms

This is a complicated engraved full panel armorial with twin helmets and crests. The shield surrounded by the motto and badge of the Royal Victorian Order. Signed and dated bottom left. The plate occurs in black and dark brown and was engraved by Downey.

ARMS: Quarterly, 1 and 4, Sable, two bendlets argent between three cross crosslets fitchee in pale of the last

H088

(Harford), 2 and 3, Azure, a saltire paly ermine and or, between two rams passant in pale of the second and as many cross crosslets fitchee in fess argent (Battersby), An escutcheon in pretence, Quarterly, 1, Sable, a bend or between six fountains (Stourton), 2, Gules, on a bend between six cross crosslets fitchee argent an inescutcheon or charged with a demi lion pierced through the mouth with an arrow all within a double tressure flory and counterflory gules (Howard), 3, Gules, three lions passant guardant in pale or, a label of three points argent (Plantagenet), 4, Sable, a chevron between three estoiles argent (Langdale).

CRESTS:

1. On a wreath of the colours, in front of flames, issuant therefrom a phoenix proper, two cross crosslets fitchee in saltire argent (Harford).
2. On a wreath of the colours issuant out of fire proper, a dragon's head per pale or and azure between a pair of wings ermine (Battersby).

MOTTO: 'Inter utrumque tene' – Keep between the two.

Frederic Dundas Harford was born on 8 February 1862 the second son of John Battersby Harford (1819–75) of Blaise Castle, Gloucestershire and his wife, Mary Charlotte, daughter of H.E. Baron de Bunsen, Prussian Minister at the Court of St James.

He was educated at Harrow and Christ Church, Oxford and entered the Diplomatic Service. He served in numerous embassies around the world and was the British delegate at the 'Wild Bird Protection Conference' in Paris in 1895. He was a Justice of the Peace and Deputy Lieutenant for Cardiganshire and created a Commander of the Royal Victorian Order (CVO) in 1906. He retired in 1916.

He married, 1896, Amy Mary Josephine daughter and co-heir of Henry Stourton JP of Holme Hall, Yorkshire. They had one daughter, Joan Mary, who married, 1920, Sir Alexander Bannerman Bart. They lived at Glebe House, Brackley, Northants. and in London.

He died on 28 April 1931.

H089 1909 Alfred Middleton Rickards 10.3 × 8.4 cms

This is a pictorial/armorial plate. Through a pillared archway with broken pediment is seen a ruined mediaeval castle. This is almost certainly Ludlow Castle in Shropshire. Upon the design, without complete tincture lines, are four coats of arms: in base – the arms of the City of London, Argent, a cross of St George gules, in the first quarter a sword erect point upwards of the second. On the left hand pillar – the arms of the town of Ludlow, Azure, a lion couchant between three roses argent. On the right hand pillar – the arms of the county of Shropshire, Ermine, three piles azure, the middle one reversed, each bearing a leopard's head affrontee or. On the pediment are the arms of the Law Society of England and Wales, with supporters and motto, which were granted in 1845. In heraldic terms they are slightly complicated and somewhat puzzling, Ermine, on a cross gules a sword sheathed, in pale point upwards or; on a chief of the last, a pale of the second charged with a lion passant guardant of the third, between a lion rampant or on the dexter side and a harp azure on the sinister side. The motto – 'Leges juraque servamus' translates as, 'We preserve laws and rights'. It is rather odd to find on the arms of the Law Society of England and Wales the lion rampant of Scotland, the harp of Ireland and nothing to denote Wales.

Alfred Middleton Rickards was born in 1874. He married, in September 1899, Eva Maria Meats (born 1872) who was known as Molly. By 1911 the family had moved to Hampstead in North London. From the design of the bookplate and the arms displayed I would surmise he was born in Shropshire probably in Ludlow and later moved to London where he practiced as a solicitor. He may have met Helard professionally through her husband or geographically through family connections. The bookplate is signed and dated along the bottom edge.

H090 1910 *Philipp Schey de Koromla* 11.4 × 8.2 cms

A fine, engraved full panel armorial for an Austrian baron. Printed in dark brown and engraved by Downey it is signed and dated at the right hand end of the name scroll.

ARMS: On a bend between an eagle displayed in base and a lion rampant in chief, two estoiles of eight points, (due to the lack of tincture lines it is not possible to blazon the arms more accurately from this engraving). The shield surmounted by his coronet of rank as an Austrian baron and supported by an eagle and a lion rampant.

CRESTS:
Three crests are shown, each rising out of a coronet.
1. A demi eagle displayed.
2. an estoile of eight points.
3. A demi lion rampant.

Philipp Schey von Koromla (1798–1881), a merchant and philanthropist and the owner's grandfather, was raised to the Austrian peerage by Letters Patent granted 13 May 1859 by the Emperor Francis Joseph I for his services to the Imperial dynasty during the Revolution in 1848–9 and also for 'the great benevolence shown by him to suffering humanity regardless of creed'.

He had a son Paul, the 2nd baron born 1854 who married, in 1878, Evalina Landauer. They had three daughters and a son Philipp, the owner of this plate, born 1881 and who married in 1906, Lili Jeanette von Goldschmidt-Rothschild and later inherited his father's title as the 3rd baron. At some stage the family exchanged the German 'von' for the French 'de'.

He died in 1929.

H089 (95%)

H090

H091

H090a 1910 Philipp Schey de Koromla 8.7 × 6.3 cms

A smaller but identical plate printed in a lighter shade of brown and also engraved by Downey.

H090b 1910 Philipp Schey de Koromla

An engraved design of a similar size to H90a but on a larger plate and printed in black. Not signed or dated.

H091 1913 Charles Stuart Forbes 9.2 × 7.0 cms

Engraved by Downey this is a full panel armorial printed in dark brown with the motto above and the name scroll below. It is signed and dated at the bottom right corner.

ARMS: Quarterly, 1 and 4, Azure three bears heads couped argent muzzled gules (Forbes), 2 and 3, Azure, three cinquefoils or fraises argent (Fraser), in the centre point a crescent for difference.

CREST: On a wreath of the colours, a falcon rising proper.

MOTTO: 'Altius ibunt qui ad summa nituntur' – They will rise higher who aim at the greatest things.

The arms, crest and motto borne are those of the baronetcy of Forbes of Newe, created 1823 with a crescent for difference. The 5th baronet was Sir Charles Stuart Forbes (1867–1928) who succeeded his father in 1884. The presence of a cadency mark in the centre point would indicate that the owner of this plate must be a cadet member of the family with the same name.

H092

H092a

FELIX QUI PRUDENS

Thomas Herbert Wood

H093

H092 1915 Albert Davidson 11.6 × 6.5 cms

A large engraved panel armorial with motto over and name scroll below, a thistle in each top corner. It is signed and dated at the right hand of the name scroll. The plate occurs in black and brown and was engraved by Downey.

ARMS: Sable, on a cross or between two pheons in pale of the first a label of three points gules.

CREST: On a wreath of the colours a stag sejeant with wings endorsed or.

MOTTO: 'Tace aut face' – Keep silence or act.

Albert Davidson was born in 1869 the second son of John Davidson of Meersbrook, Heeley, Sheffield (1837–82) and his wife, Harriet, daughter of John Biggins of Heeley, Sheffield. He trained as a mechanical engineer and, later, was the managing director of Hattersley and Davidson Ltd. He became a Commander of the Most Excellent Order of the British Empire (CBE) in 1918.

He married firstly 1892, Alice Maud (died 1894), eldest daughter of William Barker of Hatfield. They had two sons, Albert, born 1893 and John, born 1894 killed in France, 1917.

He married secondly 1896, Emma, eldest daughter of William Birks and had a further three sons, Henry Herbert (H096), born 1897, Philip, born 1901 and Alan, born 1909. The family lived at Tulloch House, Norton Woodseats, Sheffield. He died on 24 March 1932.

H092a Albert Davidson 4.5 × 3.0 cms

Small ink and wash sketch, simple armorial with shield, crest and motto with pencilled name under. It is not known if this was ever printed as a bookplate.

H093 1916 Thomas Herbert Wood 8.9 × 7.0 cms

An engraved full panel armorial with name scroll surrounding the base with a traditionally facing helmet and crest. Nice design but lack of tincture lines makes identification difficult.

ARMS: Per chevron ?argent and ermine, on a chevron between in chief two stags heads erased and in base an oak sprig, a rose between two fleur-de-lis.

CREST: A lion rampant holding in his dexter paw a wreath, the sinister resting on a staff raguly.

MOTTO: 'Felix qui prudens' – Happy is he who is prudent.

Nothing has been discovered concerning the owner.

H094 1917 Lord Wharton (8th Baron) 11.5 × 9.0 cms

This is an extremely fine full panel armorial with supporters for a peer of the realm. Vertical impaled shield with coronet of rank and two crested helmets, motto scroll in base. Signed and dated bottom right. Unusually, the plate bears no name which originally made identification difficult due to the lack of tincture lines.

ARMS: Quarterly, 1 and 4, Quarterly, 1 and 4, Gules, a lion couchant between six cross crosslets argent (Tynte), 2 and 3, Vert, on a chevron argent, three pheons sable (Kemeys), 2 and 3, Sable, a maunch argent, a bordure or, charged with eight pairs of lions gambs erased saltirewise gules (Wharton), impaling, Erminois, a cross sable charged with five crescents argent (Ellis). The dexter supporter is a bull rampant and the sinister supporter a lion rampant.

CRESTS:
1. On a wreath of the colours, on a mount vert a unicorn sejeant sable, armed, crined and unguled or (Tynte).
2. A bull's head erased sable, ducally gorged or (Wharton).

MOTTO: 'Plaisir en faits d'armes'.

Charles Theodore Halswell Kemeys-Tynte was born on 18 September 1876, the eldest son of Halswell Milborne Kemeys-Tynte and his wife, Rosabelle, daughter of Theobald Walsh of Tyrrelstown, County Kildare.

He married, 1899, Dorothy, the youngest daughter of Major General Sir Arthur Ellis KCVO, Equerry to King Edward VII 1901, and his wife, Mina Labouchere, daughter of the 1st Baron Taunton.

Sir Thomas Wharton was created Baron Wharton of Wharton in Westmoreland in 1544 under Henry VIII. Much argument has ensued over the centuries as to whether the creation was by Letters Patent, with remainder to the heirs male or by Writ with general remainder to descendents. It was argued originally that the Barony was created by Letters Patent and therefore became extinct on the death of the 6th Baron Wharton, (by then raised in the Peerage to the Dukedom of Wharton) without issue in 1731.

In 1845 Charles Kemeys-Tynte and other descendents of the 4th Baron Wharton claimed before a Committee of Privileges that the Barony was by Writ and therefore descendible to heirs general. This claim was upheld but

nothing further was done on that occasion. A Committee of Privileges in 1915 confirmed the decision of 1845 although the decision was seen by some as controversial. As a result of the decision the alleged abeyance of the Barony was terminated in favour of Charles Theodore Halswell Kemeys-Tynte by the issue of a Writ of Summons to Parliament as 8th Baron Wharton, 15 February 1916.

Lord Wharton lived at Halswell Park, Bridgewater, Somerset and at Chelway Court, Bristol.

He died on 4 March 1934 and was succeeded by his son Charles.

H095 1917 Lady (Dorothea) Wharton

8.6 × 8.0 cms

This is a highly decorative heraldic plate, without tincture lines, which is somewhat confusing, armorially speaking, on first sight. The arms in centre chief in a lozenge suspended from a knotted ribbon are the arms of the owner as a maiden lady but this lady had been married for eighteen years when this plate was made. It belongs to Dorothea, 8th Lady Wharton.

ARMS: In centre chief, in a lozenge, Erminois, a cross sable charged with five crescents argent (Ellis) suspended above a coronet of rank for a baroness supported by a bull rampant and a lion rampant, below which is a scrolled and entwined ribbon in the form of the letters D, K and T (Dorothea Kemeys-Tynye).

To the dexter side the three shields are, from top to bottom:

Gules, a lion couchant between six cross crosslets argent (Tynte).

Vert, on a chevron argent three pheons sable (Kemeys).

Sable, a maunch argent, a bordure or charged with eight pairs of lions gambs erased saltirewise gules (Wharton).

And on the sinister side from top to bottom:

Gules, on a bend argent three trefoils slipped vert (Harvey).

Gules, two lions passant argent (ducally crowned or, not shown) (Felton).

Gules, on a bend between six cross crosslets fitchee argent, on an escutcheon a demi lion rampant erased, pierced through the mouth with an arrow within a double tressure flory counter flory all gules (Howard).

The shields to the dexter represent her husband's forebears and those to the sinister her own forebears.

Dorothea Ellis was the youngest daughter of Major General Sir Arthur Ellis KCVO and his wife, The Hon. Mina Labouchere, daughter of the first Lord Taunton. She married, in 1899, Charles Theodore Halswell Kemeys-Tynte who was later (1916) restored to the peerage as the 8th Baron Wharton – see H094.

H096 1919 Henry Herbert Davidson 7.5 × 4.7 cms

A full panel armorial printed in brown with no use of tincture lines. The shield is canted, with traditional placing of helmet and crest. It is signed and dated at the bottom right hand.

ARMS: Sable, on a cross or between two pheons in pale, a label of three points gules. In centre chief a crescent for difference.

CREST: On a wreath of the colours a stag sejeant wings endorsed or.

MOTTO: 'Tace aut face' – Keep silence or act.

Henry Herbert Davidson MA was born in 1897 the third son of Albert Davidson (H092) and his second wife, Emma, daughter of William Birks. The reason he uses a crescent for difference, the mark of a second son, is that one of his elder brothers, John, was killed in France in 1917 thus promoting him to second son living (see below). He was educated at Balliol College, Oxford and entered the army becoming a Lieutenant in the Royal Garrison Artillery, a sub group of the Royal Artillery founded in 1899, the other sub groups being the Royal Horse Artillery and the Royal Field Artillery. They were all amalgamated as the Royal Artillery in 1924.

H096a Henry Herbert Davidson 9.4 × 6.0 cms

Pencil sketch, traditional full panel armorial, for a bookplate but showing a mullet in centre chief, cadency mark for a third son. Possibly this drawing was done pre 1917 when his elder brother, John, was still alive or was one of a number of designs from which the final choice, H096, was made. It is not known as a printed bookplate.

H096

H096a

H096b

H097

H096b Henry Herbert Davidson 8.0 × 8.4 cms

Another sketch with helmet and crest set to one side of the shield, again showing the cadency mark of a third son, probably produced at the same time as the previous sketch. Again, not known as a printed bookplate.

H097 1920 Sidney Rupert Payne 9.0 × 6.4 cms

An engraved full panel armorial with canted shield and helmet slightly turned. The motto is above and the name scroll below. The mantling is typical of Helard. Lack of tincture lines and the fact that the arms are not listed in any standard work of reference make full blazoning impossible. It is signed and dated bottom right.

ARMS: Per chevron, in chief two lions rampant, in base three rowels two and one.

CREST: On a wreath of the colours a demi talbot holding in its paws a sword entwined with an oak branch.

MOTTO: 'Vive ut vivas' – Live that you may have life.

Sidney Rupert Payne lived in Birmingham and was an artist. He married Mabel Wilmot the daughter of a well known Birmingham jeweller in Solihull in 1911. They had two sons, John Wilmot Payne born in 1912 and Richard Wilmot Payne born in 1915.

H098 1922 Emily Mathews Gibb 8.3 × 6.2 cms

This is a panel armorial for a widow with the arms in a lozenge suspended from a knotted ribbon surrounded by the arms of Judge, Poyntz, Edwards and Kynaston. The motto is above and the name below. It is signed and dated at the bottom right. It is doubtful if the arms in the main shield are borne with lawful authority as they belong to neither the Gibb nor the Matthews families.

ARMS: Barry of eight or and gules (Poyntz), on an escutcheon of pretence, sable a chevron ermine between three escallops argent (Judge).

MOTTO: 'Totem (sic) (? Totum) est providentia' – Everything by providence.

Emily Judge Matthews was the daughter of John Judge Matthews. She married, 1884, John Richmond Gibb of New York. (He died 1906). They had one son, John Richmond Gibb born 1891.

H098

H099 1922 Henry George Charles, Viscount Lascelles 10.5 × 9.7 cms

This is probably the finest of all Helard's plates, produced, for Lord Lascelles, the eldest son of the Earl of Harewood, in 1922, the year in which he married Mary, the Princess Royal, only daughter of King George V and Queen Mary. It depicts the conjoined arms of Harewood and the Royal Arms, differenced, for a child of the Monarch, with a Harewood supporter (a bear ermine) to the dexter side and a Royal supporter (a unicorn) to the sinister. The helmet is correctly shown as that of a knight (of the Garter) because his Viscountcy is a courtesy title in right of his father and not a peerage in its own right. It is signed and dated bottom right and occurs in black and dark brown.

ARMS: Sable, a cross patonce within a bordure or, overall a label of three points for difference (eldest son) the escutcheon surrounded by the Garter with motto from which depend his Lordship's other honours and placed accollee with the Royal Arms with a label of three points each charged with a cross for difference, surrounded by a wreath and surmounted by a coronet denoting a child of the Sovereign.

CREST: A bear's head couped at the neck ermine, muzzled gules, buckled or and gorged with a collar of the second rimmed and studded gold, a label of three points for difference.

MOTTO: 'Ung Roy, ung Foy, ung Loy' – One King, one Faith, one Law.

Henry George Charles Lascelles was born on 9 September 1882 the eldest son of Henry Ulick Lascelles GCVO, 5th Earl of Harewood and his wife, Florence Katherine, daughter of the 3rd Earl of Bradford.

He was educated at Eton and the Royal Military College. He was a Captain in the Grenadier Guards, fought in the 1914–18 War and was awarded the DSO and bar.

He married, 28 February 1922, HRH Princess Victoria Alexandra Alice Mary, the Princess Royal. He succeeded to his father's titles as 6th Earl of Harewood in 1929. He was a Justice of the Peace for the West Riding of Yorkshire and Lord Lieutenant 1927. He served in numerous other public offices including King's Trustee of the British Museum. The family estate is Harewood House, Leeds, Yorkshire. He also owned properties in Galway, Ireland and Newmarket, Suffolk.

H099

H100

H100 1922 Robert George Bartlett Mansfield-Haysom 8.4 × 6.2 cms

An engraved full panel armorial with quartered coat and two crests. It is printed in brown with an absence of tincture lines. The motto is above and the name scroll below. Signed and dated outside the panel at the bottom right. It is illustrated in *Armorial Families* seventh edition, volume 2.

ARMS: Quarterly, 1 and 4, Argent, two barrulets between six cinquefoils, three, two and one sable (Haysom), 2 and 3, Argent on a chevron, between three maunches sable, a heart or (Mansfield).

CRESTS:

1. On a wreath gules and argent, a demi griffin sable, collared and holding between the claws a harp or (Haysom).
2. On a wreath of the colours, a griffin's head erased sable holding in the beak a heart or (Mansfield).

MOTTO: 'Serus in coelum redeas' – You will return to heaven late.

Robert George Bartlett Mansfield-Haysom was born in 1874 the second son of John Mansfield-Haysom of Ringwood, Hampshire and his wife, Mary Annie, daughter of Robert George Bartlett of Branscombe, Devon.

He married firstly, 1899, Emma, died 1909, daughter of Thomas Hussey, of Ilchester Manor House, Somerset, secondly, 1911, Emma Aplin, died 1922 and, thirdly, 1923, Florence Charlotte Emma, Lady of the Manors of Burstock and Sadborow, Dorset, daughter of J.W. Hawkesworth and widow of Captain John Bragg.

H101 1922 Reginald Monckton 10.2 × 7.2 cms

A large engraved full panel armorial with a staff to the dexter side, banner above, depicting arms, badge, crest and motto, and name scroll below. The closed helmet, almost forward facing, has the crest correctly orientated. Signed and dated outside the panel at bottom right. The plate occurs in black and dark brown. It is illustrated in *Armorial Families* seventh edition, volume 2.

ARMS: Or, three bars and in chief as many mullets vert.

CREST: On a wreath of the colours, a demi cluniac monk habited holding in the dexter hand a scourge with four knotted lashes all proper.

MOTTO: 'God bless le Moigne'.

Reginald Monckton was born in 1877 the only son of Henry Monckton of Aller Court, Somerset and his wife, Elizabeth, daughter of Richard Evans of Aller, Somerset.

He married in 1906, Gertrude Olivia, eldest daughter of Colonel A.H. Hobbs of The Mount, Saltford, Somerset. They had one son, Anthony Reginald le Moigne Monckton and two daughters. The family seat was, le Moigne's, Wrington, Somerset.

H101

H101a 1922 Reginald Monckton 5.6 × 4.2 cms

A much smaller engraved plate depicting helmet, crest, motto and mantling with the name scroll below. It occurs in black and dark brown and is signed and dated at the bottom right.

CREST: On a wreath of the colours, a demi cluniac monk habited holding in the dexter hand a scourge with four knotted lashes all proper.

MOTTO: 'God bless le Moigne'.

H102 1926 Alexander Spreckley Raworth, Seigneur de St Jean 13.3 × 8.7 cms

This is one of Helard's largest and finest plates and is in the form of a panel pictorial armorial. It has a full achievement with name scroll below and a view of the Manor of St Jean with lake and boat at the top. Signed and dated at the bottom right. It was engraved by Downey and illustrated in *Armorial Families* seventh edition, volume 2.

ARMS: Gules, on a fess dancettee argent between six cross crosslets fitchee or, three anchors sable, on a quarter, also

H101a

H102

sable three eagles displayed argent (Raworth); impaling Argent, on a fess azure between, in sinister chief and in base an escallop gules, three mullets or, a quarter of the third charged with four fusils conjoined in fess of the first.

CREST: Issuant out of a coronet composed of three fleur-de-lis set upon a rim or, a demi lion proper, semi of estoiles, holding in the paws a cross crosslet fitchee gold.

MOTTO: 'Fide et constantia' – By fidelity and constancy.

Alexander Spreckley Raworth was born on 30 August 1869, the son of John Thomas Raworth of Norwood, Surrey and his wife, Susannah, daughter of James Wiggington of The Lodge, Norton, Leicestershire.

He was the holder of the Feudal Fiefdom and Seigneurie de St. Jean la Hougue Boete, Jersey (first granted to Drogo de Barentine in 1215) confirmed on him by HM King George V in 1921. The Fief owes fealty twice yearly at the Assize d'Heritage of the Royal Court and personal homage on the visit of the Sovereign.

He married Anne Elizabeth, daughter of Edwin Snowden and they lived at The Manor of St Jean, Jersey.

H103

H104

H103　1930　Moyra de Somery Fox-Davies

8.6 × 5.2 cms

This is a half tone block print armorial for a single lady, the artist's daughter. Signed and dated at bottom right. The arms are surmounted by the family badge, a crown vallery gules, and suspended from a knotted ribbon.

ARMS: In a lozenge, Sable , a semi-sun in splendour issuant in base or, a chief dancettee of the last. The arms were granted on the 26 December 1905.

BADGE: A crown vallery gules, granted 20 December 1921.

Moyra de Somery Fox-Davies was born 17 October 1903, the eldest child and only daughter of the artist and her husband Charles Fox-Davies. Her godmother was the Countess of Yarborough (see H052). She married, in 1934, Robert Regan, a hospital secretary and they had one daughter, Nicola, born 15 May 1941. She assisted her father in the production of his magnum opus, *Armorial Families*. Particularly with the final, seventh edition, in two volumes, 1929–30, which were published after his death in 1928.

Moyra died in London, 10 January 1972.

H104　1930　Cecil Kahn　7.6 × 5.7 cms

A half tone block plate depicting a sheaf of foliage looking rather like pseudo mantling surrounded by scattered piles of books and a lamp which is lit, representing knowledge. All within a gothic arch at the top of which are the arms of Trinity College, Cambridge.

'Argent, a chevron between three roses gules barbed and seeded proper and on a chief gules a lion passant guardant between two closed books or'.

Across the top is the phrase 'Neither a borrower nor a lender be' The name is on a bundle of oak leaves at the bottom. It is signed and dated at the bottom right.

Cecil Harry Kahn was born on 10 May 1901 the eldest child of Harry and Cecile Kahn of 18 Queens Gate Gardens, London S.W. In 1911 the family were living there in some style with seven indoor servants. A sister, Sybil had been born in 1906 (see H105). The father was a director of a Finance Company and a Trust Company.

Cecil married Agnes R.F. Pollitzer in Hampstead, London in 1927. Judging by the bookplate he graduated from Trinity College, Cambridge.

He died in Surrey in January 1991 aged ninety years.

H105　1930　Sybil Margaret Kahn　5 cms diameter

A half tone block plate in the form of a floral roundel with name cartouche at the bottom. Threaded through the flowers is a long ribbon on which the phrase, running clockwise reads – 'I love to lose myself in other men's minds'. The same phrase is used in the plate for Mary Helen Jenkins (H085). Signed and dated bottom right.

Sybil Margaret Kahn was the sister of Cecil Kahn (H104). She was born in 1906, the daughter of Harry and Cecile Kahn. The year after this plate was made she married Gerald C. Jacobson in Marylebone, London.

H105

H106 1930 Sir Hector Livingston Duff 10.8 × 7.8 cms

This is a half tone block, full panel armorial for a knight of the realm. The shield surrounded by the motto of The Most Excellent Order of the British Empire from which is suspended the badge of the order and the badge of the Order of St Michael and St George. The family motto is on a ribbon stretching behind the helmet and his badge is in the top right and left corners. Signed and dated bottom right.

ARMS: Per fess dancettee vert and ermine, in chief a stag's head caboshed between two escallops or.

CREST: On a wreath of the colours, between two wings erect argent, each enfiled by a wreath of laurel leaves vert, an eagle's head erased sable.

BADGE: (Officially granted in commemoration of maternal descent from the Lords Livingston of Callendar) – A cinquefoil gules charged with a bee volant or.

MOTTO: 'Tout ce que je puis' – Everything that I can.

Hector Livingston Duff was born 10 January 1872 the son of John Pope Duff (1826–74) of Edderton House, Edderton and his wife, Alice, daughter of William Sewell of Quebec and widow of General Sir Edward Russell (see H107) of Ashford Hall, Ludlow.

He joined the Diplomatic Service and was Chief Secretary to the Government of Nyasaland with a seat on the Legislative Council and was frequently Acting Governor and Commander in Chief. He was created a Companion of The Most Distinguished Order of St Michael and St George (CMG) in 1915 and made a Knight Commander of The Most Excellent Order of the British Empire (KBE) in 1918. He was called to the Bar by the Inner Temple in 1919.

He died on 10 February 1954.

H106

H107 1930 General Sir Edward Lechmere Russell
10.8 × 6.0 cms

A full panel armorial produced from a half tone block with the motto above and the name scroll below. The shield is surrounded by the motto, ribbon and badge of The Most Exalted Order of the Star of India. It is signed and dated at the bottom right.

Although the date is quite clear, the strange thing is that this plate appears to have been produced posthumously twenty-six years after the owner's death. It should be noted that his widow later married Sir Hector Livingston Duff (H106) and the two plates were produced in the same year.

ARMS: Granted 18 August 1820, – Argent, on a chevron between three cross crosslets fitchee sable, an eagle's head erased or, a bordure engrailed gules charged with eight plates.

CREST: On a wreath of the colours a demi lion rampant charged with a fasces proper and holding in his dexter paw a cross crosslet fitchee sable.

MOTTO: 'Sub cruce salus' – Salvation by the Cross.

Edward Lechmere Russell was born in 1818. He married, 1876, Alice, daughter of William Sewell, Sheriff of Quebec, Canada. They had two daughters, co-heirs, Gwendoline and Winifred Penelope. He entered the Indian Army in 1837, served in Sind and Afghanistan 1842–3 and the Abyssinian War 1863. He was made a General in 1877 and later created Knight Commander of the Star of India (KCSI) 1868. The family seat was Ashford Hall, Ludlow, Shropshire.

He died on 30 January 1904 having retired to Lansdown Crescent, Bath.

H108 1930 George Patrick Wickham-Legg
6.7 × 5.0 cms

A rather poor quality, full panel, armorial produced from a half tone block, with motto above and name scroll below. It is signed and dated at the bottom right.

ARMS: Sable, on a pile or between two books argent, in base, clasped and garnished of the second, a leg in armour, couped at the thigh, of the field, spurred and garnished gold.

CREST: On a wreath of the colours, a dexter arm in armour sable, garnished gold holding in the hand a roll of paper argent, between two roses or.

MOTTO: 'Tolle lege' – Take up and read.

George Patrick Wickham-Legg was born in 1899 the only son of Sir George Edward Wickham-Legg (1870–1927) KBE, MVO and his wife, Kathleen Octavia, eldest daughter of Sir James Gildea GBE, KCVO. He became a lieutenant in the 3rd Battalion, South Staffordshire Regiment.

H109 1931 Anthony Browning Coote 6.8 × 4.5 cms

A panel armorial with gothic arch top, from a half tone block, signed and dated bottom right.

ARMS: Argent a fess sable between three coots close proper.

CREST: On a wreath of the colours a coot's head erased proper.

MOTTO: 'Vincit veritas' – Truth prevails.

Anthony Browning Coote was born on 12 December 1905 at Torbay in Devon. He married, in 1931, Marjorie W. Neill. In 1956 he moved to Rainbow Cottage, Ashton, near Exeter.

He died at Torbay in 1979.

H110 1931 Richard Jeffries Mortimer Spranger
6.5 × 3.5 cms

A small panel armorial plate produced from a half tone block. Untypical stylised mantling with name scroll. Signed and dated outside panel bottom right.

ARMS: Per pale argent and sable, three fleur-de-lis counterchanged.

CREST: On a wreath of the colours, out of a ducal crown, a fleur-de-lis argent between a pair of eagle's wings.

Richard Jeffries Mortimer Spranger was born on 30 September 1911 the eldest son and third child of Francis Jeffrey Spranger, barrister-at-law and his wife Mary Ferris nee Mortimer. His parents were married in 1900 at Romsey in Hampshire. He had two older sisters Dora and Joan and in 1911 the family were living at 27 Pembroke Road, Kensington, London.

He died in February 1989 in Surrey.

H107

H108

H109

H110

H111 1932 Richard F.E. Ferrier 8.6 × 6.7 cms

A simple full armorial produced from a half tone block, quarterly of eight, motto in scroll at base. Signed and dated bottom right hand of shield.

ARMS: Quarterly, 1 and 8, Vair or and gules, on a bend sable three horseshoes argent (Ferrier), 2, Argent, a cross engrailed gules, on a canton also gules a saltire engrailed or and, on a chief of the last three cross crosslets of the first (Longe), [the last charge does not appear to be shown but may be concealed by the helmet], 3, Argent, an eagle displayed azure (Waunci), 4, Argent, a chevron between three squirrels sejeant gules (Lovell), 5, Sable, a cross between four lions rampant or (Bendish), 6, Vert, two chevrons argent each charged with three cinquefoils gules (Muswell), 7, Azure, a maunch or (Conyers).

CREST: On a wreath of the colours a horse's head erased argent, charged with a bend vair or and gules.

MOTTO: 'Ferrum' – A sword.

Richard Frederick Ernest Ferrier was born in 1865, the eldest son of Frederick William Ferrier (1828–96) solicitor and his wife, Mary Ann, youngest daughter of the Reverend Thomas Henry Hawes, rector of Burgh Castle, Suffolk.

He also was a solicitor and a Justice of the Peace for Norfolk. He was Lord of the Manor of Hemsby and Lay Rector and Patron of the living. He was an Alderman and served as Mayor for the Borough of Great Yarmouth 1923–4.

He married, 1895, Madelaine Lucy younger daughter of the Reverend George Bennett. They had two sons and one daughter. The elder son became a solicitor like his father and grandfather. The younger son went into the Navy and was, sadly, killed in action in 1917 at the age of only eighteen. The family seat was at Hemsby Hall, Hemsby, Norfolk.

H111

H112

H112 1932 H.S. and E.M. London 8.2 × 6.6 cms

A full panel armorial produced from a half tone block, a joint plate for a husband and wife. Signed and dated, indistinctly, bottom right hand corner. No tincture lines.

ARMS: Azure, five lozenges conjoined in bend between two crosses patee fitchee or.

CREST: On a wreath of the colours, a lozenge chequey argent and sable between two wings or.

MOTTO: 'Virtus non stemma' – Virtue not pedigree.

Hugh Stanford London was born on 3 April 1884 the elder son of Sir Stanford London and his wife, Marion, daughter of Septimus Luff of Parkstone, Dorset.

He was educated at Dulwich College and Clare College, Cambridge and went into the Diplomatic Service. He was Vice-Consul at Zanzibar, 1908 and Algiers 1912, later he was Consul General in Paris and then New Orleans. He was a Member of the Royal Commission on Historical Monuments. He was a student of heraldry and assistant editor of The New Dictionary of British Arms. He designed bookplates for friends and many for himself. He was appointed Norfolk Herald Extraordinary for the 1953 Coronation.

He married, 1913, Edith Madelaine, eldest daughter of Charles Wilkins of Edgbaston. They lived, latterly, at Coldharbour, Buxted near Uckfield, Sussex.

He died 20 January 1959.

H113

H113 1932 Mary G.C. Neave 11.6 × 6.8 cms

This is a half tone block panel armorial for an unmarried lady. The arms are on a lozenge suspended from a knotted ribbon with motto above. It is signed and dated at the bottom right.

ARMS: Argent, on a cross sable five fleur-de-lis or.

MOTTO: 'Sola proba quae honesta' – The things which are honourable alone are good.

Mary Gertrude Catherine Neave was born on 21 September 1877 the eldest child of Sir Arundell Neave 4th Baronet, (1829–77) who, on 26 September 1871 had married The Hon. Gwyn Gertrude Hughes youngest daughter of the 1st Lord Dinorben.

The family home was at Dagnams Park, Essex. She was second cousin to Airey Neave MP (1916–79) who was assassinated by the IRA in the Palace of Westminster.

H114 1932 Alan Kennedy Whitefoord 7.6 × 5.5 cms

A half tone block, full panel armorial without the use of tincture lines. It is one of the last of the dated plates and is signed and dated at bottom right.

ARMS: A bend cottised sable between two wheat sheaves.

CREST: On a wreath of the colours a wheat sheaf crowned with a pheasant.

MOTTO: 'D'en haut' – From above.

Alan Kennedy Whitefoord is descended from the Whitefoords of Blairquhan, Ayrshire, Scotland. His grandfather, Dr Adam John Whitefoord was born in London on 5 April 1846 and became a doctor in St John's Wood. He married, 4 December 1873, Ellen Mary Cole and they had three children the eldest of whom was Lionel Cole Whitefoord who married Marjorie Agatha Postlethwaite. They were the parents of Alan who was born on 28 July 1908. He was educated at Eastbourne College, Eastbourne but died in 1932, the year this plate was made, at the age of only twenty-four.

H114

SECTION V

C. Helard – Undated Bookplates

These plates date between 1900 and 1932. The undated plates between 1895 and 1899 were listed, by year, in the *Ex Libris Journal* in 1899 and, therefore, can be found in Section IV. The dimensions, in centimetres, are the overall design size, not the plate size, with the vertical measurement first. Unless otherwise stated all imprints are in black.

H115 Gwerfyl Barrett 6.3 × 4.7 cms

A small panel armorial for a married lady with the impaled shield suspended from a knotted ribbon. Name ribbon below, signed at bottom right. The only known example of this plate, to date, is in the National Library of Wales.

ARMS: Sable, a chevron between three falcons heads erased argent (Barrett), impaling, Sable, a spearhead imbrued proper between three scaling ladders argent, on a chief gules a castle of the second (Lloyd).

Gwerfyl Barrett nee Lloyd was descended from the Lloyds of Danyrallt. Her grandfather was the Reverend Henry Robert Lloyd MA (1809–80), rector of Cliffe-at-Hoo. He married, 1843, Harriet, fourth daughter of the Hon. and Right Reverend Edward Grey, Bishop of Hereford and granddaughter of Charles, 1st Earl Grey.

H115

Their only son, and Gwerfyl's father, was the Reverend Iorwerth Grey Lloyd MA Exeter College, Oxford, Prebendary of Llandewi Aberarth, in the Cathedral Church of St David's. Born 21 October 1844, he married in 1871, Nina, daughter of Charles Eastland de Michele, sometime Her Britannic Majesty's Consul in St Petersburg. They had three sons and two daughters, Gwerfyl was the elder daughter. Her sister, Mabel, was a bookplate designer but for some reason Gwerfyl chose Helard to design her bookplate after her marriage to a Mr Barrett.

H116 John Holgate & Jane Batten
9.2 × 5.0 cms (excluding name)

A joint plate in the form of a simple engraved armorial with impaled shield, crest and motto.

ARMS: Per pale argent and or, three battle-axes erect sable, on a chief arched gules two cabled anchors, also erect, of the second (Batten), impaling, Azure, on a chevron argent between three bears heads couped of the last muzzled gules, a man's heart proper, a bordure or (Forbes of Monymusk).

CREST: On a wreath of the colours, in front of a dexter arm embowed in armour, the hand grasping a battle-axe in bend sinister blade upwards, two battle-axes in saltire all proper.

MOTTO: 'Boutez en avant' – Put forward.

John Holgate Batten was born in 1859 and was the only surviving son of John Batten, Principal Clerk, HM Customs.

He married, in 1892, Jane Leckie, younger daughter of Alexander Forbes of Monymusk of The Galleries, Aberdeen. They had two sons and one daughter.

John & Jane L.
Holgate & Batten.

H116

CERTUM · PETE · FINEM

WILLIAM · BILSLAND

H117

PRÆMIUM VIRTUTIS HONOR

William Henry Cox.

H118

SECUNDO CURO

Joseph Griggs, J.P., D.L.

H119

H117 William Bilsland 9.0 × 7.3 cms

An etched panel pictorial armorial plate with the arms in the centre surrounded by stems of corn, the fructed branch of an oak on which is perched a bird and at the right side a bell. The shield is placed on a mount on which are scattered thistles.

ARMS: Gules, a pair of scales between three garbs or, on a chief argent and azure, out of a cloud charged with a radiant eye, an arm in pale hand downwards grasping the scales, between two cabled anchors proper.

CREST: On a wreath of the colours, a bull's head couped sable horned gules.

MOTTO: 'Certum pete finum'(Horace) – Aim at a sure end.

It is probable that these arms were borne without lawful authority because after the award of his baronetcy he matriculated a completely different coat of arms (Debrett's Peerage 1920).

ARMS: Argent, on a fess between two bulls heads erased sable horned gules in chief and a masculues of the last in base, a salmon on its back holding a ring in its mouth proper.

CREST: A bull's head *erased* sable horned gules.

MOTTO: as above.

William Bilsland was born 17 March 1847, the son of James Bilsland, a farmer, of Ballater. He married, 1885, Agnes, third daughter of Alexander Steven of Provenside, Glasgow. He was a bread manufacturer and Chairman of Bilsland Bros. Ltd. He was also a director of the Royal Bank of Scotland.

He became Lord Provost of Glasgow and Lord Lieutenant of the City and County of Glasgow 1905–08. He was made a Knight Commander of the Norwegian Order of St Olaf in 1906 and a Member of the Imperial Japanese Order of Sacred Treasure in 1907. In the same year he was awarded an honorary LLD by the University of Glasgow and created a baronet.

In 1909 he was appointed chairman of the Scottish Departmental Committee on Inebriates. He died on 27 August 1921. He was succeeded by his son, Alexander Steven, as 2nd baronet, who rematriculated the arms shown in *Debrett*. It is almost certain that this plate dates before the award of his baronetcy in 1906.

H118 William Henry Cox 7.9 × 6.5 cms

A simple armorial, full achievement with impaled coat, motto over and name beneath.

ARMS: Or, a chevron azure between two spur rowels in chief and a lion's head erased in base gules, langued of the second, within a bordure of the third (Cox), impaling, Azure, on a chevron between three masculues or, a boar's head erased of the field, a fleur-de-lis in chief of the second (Kinloch of Gourdie).

CREST: a dexter arm embowed, issuing out of the sea, holding in the hand an anchor in bend sinister, cabled proper.

MOTTO: 'Praemium virtutis honos' – Honour is the reward of virtue.

William Henry Cox was born on 14 April 1865 the eldest son of William Cox JP of Snaigow, Perthshire and his wife, Elizabeth, daughter of Dr Henry Boase MD, FRS.

He was a Justice of the Peace for Perthshire and married, 6 June 1893, Amy Verden, daughter of William Harrower Anderson of Edinburgh. She died 21 March 1894 leaving a daughter, Amy Verdun. He married secondly, 28 April 1896, Annie, daughter of Colonel David Kinloch of Gourdie and had a son, Henry Kinloch Cox, born 6 September 1898.

He owned estates at Snaigow and Glenquaich, near Dunkeld and Clunie near Blairgowrie all in Perthshire.

H119 Joseph Griggs 8.0 × 5.6 cms

A plain armorial with motto on a separate scroll below and '*Joseph Griggs J.P., D.L.*' underneath.

ARMS: Gules, upon a pale between two feathers argent, two feathers of the field.

CREST: On a wreath of the colours, in front of two feathers crossed saltirewise gules, a sword in pale enfiled with a leopard's head proper.

MOTTO: 'Secundo curo' – I am prosperous, I am careful.

Joseph Griggs was born on 31 August 1835 the eldest son of John Griggs of Burton-on-Trent and his wife, Mary, daughter of John Dakin of Anston, Stafford. He became a Justice of the Peace and Deputy Lieutenant for Leicestershire and was High Sheriff in 1894.

He married, in 1859, Isabella, third daughter of Charles Balls of Colchester. She died in 1899 and he married secondly, in 1901, Janet, widow of Samuel Godbe. He had a son by his first wife, Frank Robertson Griggs born 1864 and a daughter Mary Isabel.

H121

H120

H120 Strangman Hancock 10.3 × 8.5 cms

A large, fine, engraved seal-type armorial with a dragon surrounding the arms and the name scroll below. The design is almost certainly taken from the well-known George Eve plate for Everard Green, Rouge Dragon, executed in 1895 and used here with equally dramatic effect but without the punning allusion.

Arms: Quarterly, 1 and 4, Ermine, a cock gules, on a chief engrailed sable three dexter hands appaumee couped at the wrist proper (Hancock), 2 and 3, Per bend sable and argent a bend embattled counter-embattled between two trefoils slipped, all counterchanged (Strangman).

Crest: On a wreath of the colours a demi lion rampant argent, charged on the shoulder with a fusil azure and holding in its paws an ogress charged with a cock of the first.

Motto: 'Vigilate et orate' – Watch and pray.

George Strangman Hancock JP of Witwatersrand District, Transvaal, South Africa was born in 1865 the second son of Thomas Strangman Hancock (1813–71) of Lisburn, Co.

Down, Northern Ireland and his wife, Emma, daughter of John Thomas Towson.

He married, in 1895, Gertrude, daughter of William Scott of Manchester and they had one son, Dugald Strangman Hancock born in 1897. The family home was Cleveland, Transvaal, South Africa.

H121 John Hill 8.3 × 6.3 cms

A fine full panel armorial with impaled coat but with lack of tincture lines. The form of the crest is absurd when one thinks of the original use of the crest but this is the fault of the Heralds granting the arms not the bookplate designer.

Arms: Ermine, on a fess nebuly per pale sable and azure, between three hillocks vert, a castle triple towered or (Hill), impaling, Gules, a chevron dovetailed ermine, on a chief or, three dragons heads erased of the first (Kirk).

Crest: On a wreath of the colours, a castle triple towered or, charged with an escutcheon azure thereon a rose argent, all between four ears of wheat, bladed and slipped or, two on either side.

Andrew Alexander Hunter.

H122

Andrew Alexander Hunter.

H122a

MOTTO: 'Avancez' – Advance.

John Hill was born on 26 August 1849 and married, 3 June 1880, Jane, daughter of William Kilvington Kirk of Stockton-on-Tees. They had two sons, John, born 8 September 1883 and Frank, born 10 April 1890.

H122 Andrew Alexander Hunter 10.0 × 8.0 cms

A simple armorial within a beaded cartouche suspended from a bow with swags, paterae and drops in the Neo-classical Adam style, with name below cartouche.

ARMS: Argent, on a chevron azure between three hunting-horns vert garnished and stringed gules, a crescent of the first.

CREST: A stag's head caboshed or.

MOTTO: 'Vigilantia robur voluptas' – Vigilance, strength, pleasure.

Andrew Alexander Hunter was born 7 August 1855, the eldest son of Major-General Andrew Hunter of the Bengal Staff Corps and his wife, Caroline, daughter of Lieutenant Colonel Nuttall Greene JP, Deputy-Lieutenant of Kilmanahan Castle, County Waterford, Ireland.

He was bursar of Cheltenham College and lived at 6 Orrisdale Terrace, Cheltenham. He was a member of the Ex Libris Society. He exhibited a photograph of the armorial bearings of Andrew Hunter, Abbott of Melrose, on a buttress at Melrose Abbey at the Society's exhibition on 14 February 1894.

H122a Andrew Alexander Hunter

There is a second version of the plate without the cartouche and suspension trappings with the name, in full, below.

H123 John Thomas Jackson 7.6 × 5.7 cms

A plain simple armorial with the motto below.

ARMS: Party per chevron azure and or in chief three pheons of the last and in base a rose gules barbed and seeded proper.

CREST: On a wreath of the colours, two pheons gules thereon an eagle with wings expanded or, each wing charged with a rose as in the arms.

MOTTO: 'Res non verba' – Deeds not words.

John Thomas Jackson was the eldest son of John Jackson of Oldham and his wife, Emma, daughter of Benjamin Goodwin of Burslem. He was a Justice of the Peace for the County Palatine of Lancaster.

He married, 16 May 1866, Sarah, second daughter of Bartholomew Prockter of Oldham. They had one son, John, born 1869, who became a lieutenant in the Lancashire Fusiliers. They lived at The Hurstead, Rochdale and Treburvaugh, Llangunllo, Radnorshire.

H124 Thomas Fielding Johnson 8.0 × 5.2 cms

A simple armorial with typical Helard mantling. The motto is on a scroll below and below that the inscription – 'Thomas Fielding Johnson, Brookfield, Leicester'.

ARMS: Argent, three chevronels between two griffins heads erased in chief and a fleece in base gules.

CREST: On a wreath of the colours a demi griffin gules, holding a pheon in the dexter claw and resting the sinister on a lozenge or.

MOTTO: 'Labore et honore' – By industry and honour.

Thomas Fielding Johnson was born 24 December 1828, the second son of John Goode Johnson of London and Stockport and his wife, Eliza, daughter of Thomas Fielding of Leicester.

William Johnson of Barkby Thorpe, Leicester a tenant at will of the Abbot and Convent of St Mary de Pratir, Leicester was living in 1296 and a pedigree has been proved, and officially recorded, showing the descent of Thomas

H123

H124

MAGNANIMITER · CRUCEM · SUSTIN

Robert Lloyd Kenyon.
of
Pradoe, Shropshire.

H125

Fielding Johnson from a William Johnson also of Barkby Thorpe who died 1572 and is buried in Barkby Church.

He was a Justice of the Peace for the city and county of Leicester. He married firstly, 3 May 1855, Julia Christina, daughter of Samuel Stone of Leicester by whom he had a son, Thomas Fielding Johnson born 24 April 1856 and, secondly, 14 April 1863, Agnes daughter of Alfred Paget of Leicester. They lived at Brookfield, Knighton, near Leicester. It is not known whether this plate is for the father or the son.

H125 Robert Lloyd Kenyon

11.4 × 8.8 cms excluding name

A large fine quartered coat but in the simple armorial style and certainly one of Helard's better pieces, with her typical mantling. The motto is on a ribbon at the base.

ARMS: Quarterly, 1, Sable, a chevron engrailed or between three crosses flory argent, 2, Sable, nine lozenges crosswise argent, overall a bend barruly argent and gules, 3, Or, on a cross flory sable five estoiles of the first, 4, Per bend ermine and erminois, a lion rampant or. There is a crescent, for difference, on the centre point.

CREST: On a wreath of the colours a lion sejeant or resting the dexter paw on a cross flory argent.

H126 (first state)

MOTTO: 'Magnanimiter crucem sustine' – Sustain the Cross bravely.

Robert Lloyd Kenyon MA, JP, DL was born on 18 January 1848 the eldest son of John Robert Kenyon QC of The Pradoe, Shropshire and his wife, Mary, daughter of Edward Hawkins, Keeper of Antiquities at the British Museum.

He was educated at Winchester and Christ Church, Oxford. He was called to the Bar by the Middle Temple, 1873, and practiced on the Oxford Circuit. He was Chairman of Shropshire Quarter Sessions, 1914–27 and Recorder of Oswestry 1896–1927.

His outside interests were in archaeology and numismatics. He edited the second and third editions of Edward Hawkins' *Silver Coins of England* 1876 and 1887 and Kenyon's *Gold Coins of England* in 1884.

He succeeded his father at The Pradoe in 1880. The house was built in 1785 for the Reverend David Pritchard incorporating an older building on the site. It was altered in 1810–16 for the then owner, the Hon. Thomas Kenyon, in whose family the property remains.

He married, 9 June 1886, Ellen, daughter of the Right Reverend William Walsham How, Bishop of Wakefield.

He died on 10 November 1931.

H126 Mount Allison Ladies College Library
9.8 × 7.2 cms

A large non armorial panel plate with a portrait, of a lady in the centre surrounded by two female figures holding a wreath above. The inscription above reads: *'Mount Allison Ladies College Library – from a fund established in 1905 by Raymond Clare Archibald in Memory of his Mother.'* Below the portrait the inscription reads: *'Mary Mellish Archibald'* and below that: *'Graduate M.L.A. 1867; Teacher 1869–71; Chief Preceptress 1871–73; Lady Principal 1885 – January 1901.'*

There are two states of this plate in the Helard Archive. The first, labelled in ink 'first proof' has the female to the right holding a blank scroll and the dates *'1899'* and *'1901'* either side of the base of the portrait. The second state which is the final version has the dates removed and the scroll filled in with – *'1849–1901'*. It occurs in black and brown. Although the plate is neither signed nor dated it probably dates shortly after 1905. Helard has done one other portrait plate that of James Tarbotton Armstrong (H042).

H126 (second state)

Harry North.

Mary Mellish was born in Pownal, Prince Edward Island in January 1849 (it is possible that the '1899' in the first proof was a mistake for '1849'). She attended Mount Allison Ladies Academy and graduated in 1867 she returned to teach mathematics there becoming Chief Preceptress in 1871.

In 1874 she married Abram Archibald and their son Raymond was born the following year. When he was only seven, in 1883, his father died and two years later his mother went back to Mount Allison as Lady Principal, a post she held until her death in 1901.

Her son, Raymond, also studied mathematics and after obtaining his doctorate at Harvard he returned to Canada becoming Professor of Mathematics at his mother's College. He also acted as College Librarian and in 1905 he founded a fund, in memory of his mother, for the purchase of new books and for which, this plate was designed.

H127 Harry North 7.5 × 5.8 cms (excluding name)

A simple armorial with name below.

ARMS: Argent, two chevronels nebuly between two mullets in chief and a decrescent in base, sable.

CREST: On a wreath of the colours a lion's head erased argent, gorged with a collar nebuly between two mullets, sable.

For details of Sir Harry North see H056. This plate was produced sometime before 1905, the year he was knighted and is illustrated, without the name, in *Armorial Families* fifth edition (1905).

H128 (Sir Richard Oldfield) 8.0 × 4.0 cms

This is an untitled plate with shield, crest and motto. Pencilled on the reverse of the print are the words '*Sir Richard Oldfield*'. This was included in the envelope of Helard plates but it is not known if it was ever titled or used as a bookplate.

ARMS: Or, on a bend invected, plain cottised gules between two Catherine wheels sable, three crosses patee fitchee argent.

CREST: On a wreath of the colours, a demi eagle displayed argent, wings semi of crosses patee fitchee gules, in front thereof a demi Catherine wheel sable.

MOTTO: 'In Deo tutamen' – In God a defence.

Richard Charles Oldfield was born on 3 November 1828 the eldest son of Henry Swann Oldfield and his wife, Letitia, daughter of Colonel Richard Scott.

He was educated at Eton and Haileybury and entered the Bengal Civil Service in 1848. He became a Judge in the High

Court of Judicature of Allahabad, India and was made a knight bachelor in 1889.

He married, 16 March 1854, Maria, daughter of Major Fredrick Angelo (she died in 1885). They had a son, Henry Oldfield (1858–1900) who became a major in the Royal Artillery and another son, Christopher born 1863, who became a captain in the Royal Artillery.

He died on 26 December 1918 at the age of ninety.

H129 Oswald Partington (2nd Lord Doverdale)

9.2 × 5.0 cms (excluding name)

An engraved simple armorial with impaled shield, crest and motto. The plate is likely to date before the creation of the peerage in 1917.

ARMS: Sable, on a bend nebuly, between four mullets of six points, two in chief and two in base argent , three Cornish choughs proper (Partington), impaling, Quarterly, 1 and 4, Or, a fetterlock azure, on a chief azure three mullets of five points argent, 2, Gules, a chevron between three crescents

H129

argent, 3, Azure, within a tressure flory counter-flory a martlet between three mullets of six points, two and one argent.

CREST: On a wreath of the colours, out of the battlements of a tower a goat's head proper charged on the neck with a mullet of six points and between two escallops sable.

MOTTO: 'Fortiter et recte' – Boldly and rightly.

Oswald Partington was born 4 May 1872, the second son of Edward Partington JP of Derby, Mayor of Glossop 1903–4 and his wife, Sarah Alcock of Bury Lancs.

Edward Partington was born in 1833. He became a Freeman, Alderman and later Mayor of Glossop. He was a director of the District Bank. He was knighted in 1912 and raised to the peerage as Baron Doverdale of Westwood Park in 1917. He died in 1925.

His son, Oswald, was educated at Rossall. He became a Justice of the Peace and Member of Parliament for the Peak division of Derbyshire 1900–10 and Member of Parliament for Shipley in the West Riding of Yorkshire 1915–18. He was Junior Lord of the Treasury 1909–10.

Due to the earlier death of his elder brother, Herbert, in 1916 Oswald succeeded to his father's title as the 2nd Lord Doverdale in 1925.

He married firstly, in 1902, the Hon. Clara Isabel Murray daughter of the 1st Viscount Elibank and had a son and a daughter. She divorced him in 1934 and he married again, the same year, Leslie, daughter of George R. Cornwell of New York and widow of James B. Tailer of New York.

He died in 1935 and was succeeded by his son, Edward, as the 3rd Lord Doverdale.

H130 Emily Paynter 9.2 × 6.6 cms

This illustration is taken from *Armorial Families* fourth edition (1902). It is also illustrated in *The Art of Heraldry* by Fox-Davies 1904 – Chapter XXXIX where it is described as '*specially designed by Miss C. Helard to illustrate the use of a ribbon for the Arms of an unmarried lady*' the owner is described as '*the late Miss Emily Paynter*' who must have died in the meantime. It has not been seen as an actual bookplate but it would, quite clearly, serve that purpose. It is signed at the right hand end of the name scroll.

ARMS: Quarterly, 1, Azure, three blocks argent each charged with an annulet sable (Paynter), 2, Azure, three faggots argent (Antron), 3, Argent, three bends gules (Bodrugan), 4, Argent, two chevronels nebuly gules

H130

H131

between three sheaves or as many arrows sable banded of the second (Best).

Emily Paynter was the youngest daughter of William Paynter of Belgrave Square and Cambourne House, Richmond, Surrey and his wife, Anne, only daughter and sole heir of Thomas Best of Hollis House, Leek, Stafford. He was a Justice of the Peace for Middlesex and Surrey and Deputy Lieutenant for Surrey.

Emily was a member of the Ladies Grand Council of the Primrose League which was where she probably came into contact with Fox-Davies who was also a member of that Conservative organisation.

H131 Richard Arthur Pease 6.1 × 4.8 cms

A fine engraved full panel armorial with a quartered coat and a label indicating the eldest son in the lifetime of his father. It is signed at the right hand end of the name scroll. This plate was probably made some time after his mother's (H082) as he would only be fifteen in 1905. It was engraved by Downey.

ARMS: Quarterly, 1 and 4, Per fess azure and gules, a fess nebuly ermine between two lambs passant in chief argent,

and in base, upon a mount proper a dove rising argent, holding in its beak a pea stalk, the blossom and pods also proper (Pease), 2 and 3, Argent, a cross engrailed sable.

CREST: On a wreath of the colours, upon the capital of an Ionic column, a dove rising, holding in the beak a pea-stalk, as in the arms, all proper.

MOTTO: 'Pax et spes' – Peace and hope.

Richard Arthur Pease was born on 18 November 1890 the son of Sir Arthur Francis Pease, 1st baronet (1920) and his wife, Laura Matilda Ethelwyn (H082) the daughter of Charles Peter Allix of Swaffham Prior House, Swaffham Prior, Cambridge. His father (1866–1927) was a coal owner, director of Pease Partners Ltd. and chairman of Durham County Council.

Richard was educated at Eton and Trinity College, Cambridge. He became a Captain in the Northumberland Yeomanry and served in the Great War (1914–18).

He married, first in 1917, Jeanette, daughter of Gustav Kissel (she died 1957) and second, 1961, Louisa Keppel, widow of Lieutenant Colonel Arnold Keppel.

He inherited his father's title, as 2nd Baronet in 1927. The family home was at Prior House, Richmond, Yorkshire.

He died on 3 November 1969.

H132 Pollard, Haynford Hall, Norwich 7.0 × 5.8 cms

An engraved plate with helmet, crest and mantling only. The motto is above and the name scroll below. This is a second plate for Rear Admiral Edwin Pollard (see H023) or possibly another member of his family. It is not listed in the *Ex Libris Journal* list in June 1899 and therefore dates sometime later. It shows the altered version of the crest with the stag collared with a naval crown and charged on the shoulder with a cross flory. The reason for the change is not known, whether it is a correction or an approved variation by the College of Arms. The description and design are quite clear in both cases.

H133 Lt. Col. George Alfred Raikes

7.2 × 5.8 cms (excluding name)

A simple engraved armorial with impaled shield

ARMS: Argent, a chevron engrailed pean between three griffins heads erased sable, each charged with an ermine spot gules (Raikes), impaling, Paly of six argent and or, a lion rampant regardant sable charged on the shoulder with a cross crosslet of the second, between four quatrefoils, two and two of the third (Morgan).

CREST: On a wreath of the colours, a griffin's head as in the arms.

MOTTO: 'Honestum praeferre utili' – I prefer what is honourable to what is useful.

George Alfred Raikes was born on 13 May 1850, the eldest son of Robert Raikes JP, DL of Eastdale, Welton, Yorkshire and his second wife, Catherine, only daughter of Michael Hart of Belmont, Co. Waterford.

He became a Lieutenant Colonel in the 3rd Battalion, the York and Lancashire Regiment and later Vice-President of the Honourable Artillery Company.

He married, on 3 September 1895, Caroline Georgina Elizabeth, the only daughter of Colonel George Manners Morgan of Biddlesden Park, Buckinghamshire.

H132

H133

Sir Thomas Lawrence Seccombe.

John Waddington.

H134 Sir Thomas Lawrence Seccombe

9.4 × 7.9 cms

An etched armorial plate for a knight surrounded by his honours and with typical Helard mantling. It is illustrated, without the name, in the fifth edition of *Armorial Families*.

ARMS: Argent, on a fess gules between three lions rampant sable, a lotus flower slipped and leaved proper, in the centre chief point an Eastern crown of the second, a bordure invected of the third.

The shield is surrounded by the collar and badge of a Knight Grand Cross of the Order of the Indian Empire. To the left is the badge of a Knight Commander of the Star of India and to the right the badge of a Commander of the Bath (Civil Division).

CREST: On a wreath of the colours a lion rampant sable between two elephants proboscides proper.

MOTTO: 'Paratus et fidelis' – Ready and faithful.

Thomas Lawrence Seccombe was born in 1812, the only son of John Seccombe and his wife, Ann, daughter of Lawrence Lee. He entered the Diplomatic Service and was Financial Secretary to the Secretary of State for India 1859–79, and Assistant Under-Secretary of State for India 1872–81.

He was created a Commander of the Bath (Civil Division) in 1869, a Knight Commander of the Star of India in 1877 and a Knight Grand Cross of the Order of the Indian Empire in 1892.

He married, 1833, Louisa, daughter of Hugh Polliett. They had five sons, three of whom predeceased him in adulthood, and one daughter, Louisa, died in 1884. The family home was at Sheridan, Newton Abbot in Devon. He died on 13 April 1902 at the age of ninety so this would have been one of Helard's earlier plates produced between 1899 and 1902.

H135 John Waddington 7.2 × 5.2 cms

This is a simple armorial plate similar in style to a number of her early plates and probably dating from the early years of the century.

ARMS: Per pale argent and gules, a fess between two fleur-de-lis in chief and a battleaxe fessways in base, blade upwards and head to the sinister, all counterchanged.

CREST: On a wreath of the colours a dexter arm embowed holding in the hand a tilting spear in bend and a battleaxe in bend sinister, all proper, the hand surmounted by a fleur-de-lis gules.

MOTTO: 'Pro recto semper' – Always for the right.

John Waddington was born, 5 April 1855, the second son of John Waddington of Leeds and his wife, Mary Anne, daughter of William Sugden of Bradford.

He trained as a civil engineer and took a leading part in the development of Western Australia. He was the original concessionaire of the Midland Railway of Western Australia and a principal pioneer of the gold and mining industries there. He was founder and chairman of The Great Boulder Proprietary Gold Mine Ltd.

He married, 29 October 1879, Evaline, daughter of George Shenton of Western Australia. They had one son and two daughters. The family homes, in England, were at Ely Grange, Frant, Sussex and Waddington Old Hall, Yorkshire. He was one of His Majesty's Lieutenants for the City of London and a Justice of the Peace for the counties of Sussex and Yorkshire. He died on 12 October 1935.

H136 T. Newby Wilson 8.2 × 7.3 cms

An engraved simple armorial plate with typical Helard trilobed mantling.

ARMS: Per chevron sable and argent, in chief a trefoil between two mullets of six points and in base a wolf rampant, all counterchanged.

CREST: On a wreath of the colours a demi wolf rampant, per chevron sable and argent, holding in the dexter paw a mullet of six points argent and resting the sinister on a trefoil slipped sable.

MOTTO: 'Fide sed cui vide' – Trust, but be cautious in whom you place it.

Thomas Newby Wilson was born 17 September 1839, the only son of Thomas Wilson of Lancaster, attorney, and his wife, Mary, daughter of Lyles Harrison of The Landing near Ulverston, Lancs.

He was a considerable landowner with twenty estates in Lancashire and five in Westmoreland. He lived at The Landing formerly his grandfather's property, at Ulverston. He was a Justice of the Peace for Lancaster.

H136

Appendix I

'Bookplates by C. Helard'

This is a leather bound album with title blocked in gold on the front and spine. It was originally in the possession of Miss Helard and when the Fox-Davies Library was sold it passed into the hands of an Ipswich book dealer who did not wish to sell it. I had an opportunity to examine it in 1978. Its present whereabouts is not known. It contains twenty-four Helard plates presumably of the artist's choosing, as her best work, covering the period 1899 to 1926. They are listed in the order in which they appeared in the album. It was by no means full should she have wished to add any of her other plates.

The Rt. Hon. Arthur Balfour PC 1899
Graeme Harrison 1900
Fredrick Dundas Harford 1909
William Ridley Richardson 1900
Marcia, Countess of Yarborough 1900
Philipp Schey de Koromla 1910
Arthur G. Soames 1899
Sir Jonathan Edmund Backhouse 1903
Helen Mary Jenkins 1906
Reginald Monckton 1922
Heber Mardon 1905
Fredric Thomas Penton 1905
A. Edmund Fraser 1900
Richard Southcote Mansergh 1901
Sir Thomas Sutherland 1900
Julian Russell Story 1906
Edith Perussi de Medici 1904
Ethelwyn Pease 1905
William Henry Watts 1901
Henry George Charles, Viscount Lascelles 1922
Sydney Rupert Payne 1920
Robert George Bartlett Mansfield-Haysom 1922
Lionel Cust 1905
Alexander Spreckley Raworth 1926

It is noted that all these plates are signed and dated and obviously considered by Helard to be her best work and worthy of a place in the album. This is born out by her comments in the Downey Correspondence (Section III) regarding the Mardon and Cust plates. The album appears to have been put together in the 1920s.

Appendix II

Letter from Arthur Charles Fox-Davies to his father, Thomas Edmond Fox-Davies, *c.*1906 concerning the newly granted family arms which had been granted to Thomas and the descendents of his father Charles Davies

Dear Father,

I had forgotten Uncle Willie [Wilbraham J.B. Casley, husband of his mother's sister, Mary Anne (Minnie) Fox.] for the moment. He is in the same position as you are as regards the Fox Arms.

One inherits one's arms from one's father, i.e. you inherit the Davies arms from your father and Jack, George and I inherit from you.

A woman ordinarily bears for life only the arms of her father and cannot ordinarily transmit them. But if she be an heiress, as Mother is, the position is different. You, as her husband, 'pretend' to the representation of her family and so you bear her arms on an escutcheon of pretence over your own but the arms really belong to Mother. She represents (as does Auntie) her own family.

Every person is a member of his father's family from birth and bears his arms in his own right as representing himself as a member of that family. Jack, George and I don't represent the Fox family Mother and Auntie do. If any of their descendents survive them the representation will fall to the descendents and the said descendents will quarter the two coats together. [Fox-Davies never had the opportunity to quarter the arms as he pre-deceased his mother-in-law, Maria Jane Fox, who died in 1937.]

That is the ordinary state of the case. But when a name is assumed by Royal Licence the Crown, by a fiction, presumes representation from the date of the assumption of the name and so, without waiting for actual representation will grant the arms with the name and you get a double name and double crest. (It is the double crest that is the real difference.)

To put things on a perfect footing I ought to have got this third Patent, as now, with a double name we are using a single coat just as if we had never taken the name of Fox at all. When the third Patent is issued there will be three coats of arms in being; (1) Davies, (2) Fox and (3) Fox-Davies. At present we are all in no better position than people who have never changed their name.

The Herald's College wanted to call only one coat into being for Fox-Davies. They first offered this to me and my descendents only but I told them I didn't care a damn to have a coat of arms if you hadn't. Then the one coat granted to you and your descendants. But I wanted the three coats and I preferred 1. and 2. to No. 3. The fees on 1. and 2. together would have been £10 more than 3. alone. But if I had taken No. 3, the double grant then Mother would have had no arms and if 1. and 2, had not previously been granted then three could never have been divided up so, as Uncle John [father's brother] has nothing to do with Fox the Fox-Davies grant would have not applied to him and as Auntie Minnie [mother's sister, Mary Ann] has nothing to do with the Davies's the Fox-Davies grant would not have applied to her. I, myself, was far keener on getting 1. and 2. than on getting 3. You will, I think, understand when you read the two Patents.

The double grant is a modern idea and not particularly good heraldry and I have not yet made up my mind whether I really want it myself. Jack says he doesn't but till I can afford the money it isn't much good troubling about the point, though I suspect I shall get it some day. But, for Moyra's sake [her brother, Harley, had not yet been born] it is more important to get grants for Crookes and Proctor. These things are a case of little by little. Now Fox and Davies have been granted separately we can join them up if we want to at any time.

With love, I remain your ever affectionate son

Charlie

Appendix III

An Account of his Forebears by Arthur Charles Fox-Davies

The following is transcribed from a manuscript account found in an exercise book and compiled, in London, during the 1st World War 1914–18. It is transcribed word for word as it was written

Why, I have no idea, but the keeping of family records has had a certain amount of fascination for me. It can hardly be the result of my work, for my work was really the consequence of my inclinations. Looking back I regret it for I have no sort or manner of doubt that had I put into some other channel the same hard work that I have expended on my books, I might and probably should have made a greater financial success of my life. But on the other hand I might not have travelled quite so far as I have got in one or two directions. If one keeps a shop, with ordinary diligence, one makes money but there are drawbacks. One cannot be proud of keeping a shop. I am glad I never did. I am proud that I am a member of the Bar, and many men far away bigger than I am ever likely to be have been proud of that. So that if it be snobbery, then I am a snob, though I am in good company.

But I admit the fascination of the chronicles of small beer. You, Harley, my son, for whose benefit – though also for my own pleasure – I am writing these lines may not care two straws about such things. Our love for each other, sonnie, rests on many matters. But if you don't care, others who come after you may do so, and therefore I write, and having written I just ask you not to destroy this. I persuaded my Father to do something of the kind himself and these minor chronicles are interesting enough, even to strangers when the lapse of time has given them the status of records.

Evelyn and Pepys never dreamed when they wrote their diaries that the world would treasure them. I don't flatter myself I am a successor of theirs but I hope there may be descendents of mine a hundred years hence who may be interested in what I write.

I have always been profoundly impressed by a certain quotation – where it comes from I am quite ignorant – 'Many things our grandfathers knew are lost to us and our grandchildren will search in vain for things which to us are most familiar.'

I was born in Bristol, 28th February 1871. Of Bristol I remember nothing, naturally so, for I was not 12 months old when my Father and Mother removed to Coalbrookdale. Of my Father's Father – my grandfather – I have no recollection. I ought to have for he did not die until 1874 and I saw him at least once when he came to visit my Father. My elder brother remembers him – I do not. His wife, my grandmother I do remember very well. She was Mary, the daughter of Rev. John Herring, a Baptist Minister of some celebrity.

My grandfather – born in Carnwarthes – was for many years in business at Cardigan – a member of the firm of Lloyd and Davies. He failed in business. I do not mean he was bankrupt but that having undertaken certain financial obligations for a relative, he had to realise his assets and was left with nothing. In the end my Father had to contribute to his support and the last few years of his life he lived at Merthyr Tydfil where he died. My Grandmother continued to live there during her widowhood and during that time she visited my Father, I think, on three occasions. He, of course, saw her frequently at Merthyr. She was a gentle kindly old soul, of whom I have nothing but the very pleasantest recollections. Her last photograph is remarkably like her.

My only other recollections of relatives on my Father's side are few. I remember my Aunts, Elizabeth and Mary – my Father's sisters. The former, who died unmarried, I think I only saw once. She was a pleasant colourless woman. My Aunt Mary in earlier years I saw a great deal of. She visited my Father and my elder brother and I visited her. My recollection of her is of a bright energetic, good natured and generous woman with some claim to good looks. I well remember her Wedding at which I was present in the Catholic Church at Madeley and I also well remember the kilt and striped silk stockings I wore on that occasion which are perpetuated in what is my earliest photograph as a kid on a rocking horse. She married Paul Verhulst a naturalised Englishman, but by birth a Belgian. He was a pleasant man with charming manners – and a man of some birth and position in Belgium. At the time of his marriage he was a prosperous drysalter in Manchester and it was there I visited them.

My chief recollection of my first visit was my first pantomime and of my second a course of riding lessons. This remains in my memory partly because at those lessons we made the informal acquaintance of the celebrated 'Belle Bilton' (afterwards Lady Dunlo and Countess of Clancarty) who with her sister at that time had a theatrical engagement in Manchester and was receiving riding lessons at the same time and place. At the time of my first visit my Aunt was living at Pendleton, and the time of my second at Heaton Chapel. Later Paul Verhulst inherited considerable sums of money from his own people and left England living first in the Channel Islands and then drifting back to Brussels. He dropped business and rapidly ran through all the money which from time to time he inherited, he and my Aunt died after, latterly, none too happy a married life in far from prosperous circumstances.

My Uncle Griffith and my Aunt Jane I never saw. The former was one time a Parliamentary Candidate but never actually fought an Election. He was Secretary to a Trade Union. The latter all that I know is that she wrote a small book of poems. My Uncle John I never saw he had settled in America. He has had a very adventurous life. His daughters, Edith, Mrs Stanley Billings and Gladys, Mrs Freeman have both visited England and stayed with my Mother, the latter bringing her two children. Both sisters have considerable ability as writers and it is quite obvious that any bent I may have towards writing and bookmaking must come from my Father's side. I never heard that any of my Mother's people ever wrote for publication but Rev John Herring for some years edited ———— my Uncle John edited ———— and was constantly writing. My Aunt wrote poems and Edith Billings and Gladys Freeman both write. I have no knowledge that my Father ever wrote more than occasional newspaper letters and a few articles but my sister Grace writes and I have myself been responsible for various books.

My Father had many relatives but I met but few of them. His 'cousin' William Henry Davies, the proprietor and Editor of the 'Cardiff Figaro' stayed with us at Coalbrook-dale with his wife, and I have met there and in her own house at Portishead my father's cousin Mrs Fulke Barnard – I cannot say I have any strong recollection of her. Some correspondence with my Father's cousin Mrs Charles Powis ended in an invitation to stay with them in Coleherne Rd, Earl's Court. Charles Powis – an Engineer – was a very amusing and engaging personality – cynical and downright but unlucky in business. He procured a Commission of Enquiry into the sanity of his brother-in-law, John Lloyd Davies a weird eccentric 'character' living at Haverfordwest. The Commission reported that he was 'sane'. He certainly did no one any harm but to put the matter mildly he was extraordinarily eccentric, and of the insanity of his mother there was no doubt. He was well-to-do, if not wealthy. After the death of Charles Powis, Mrs Powis went to live with her brother and I believe inherited his money. Of her two sons, both of whom I did meet, I have little if any recollection. They were the children of my Grandfather's brother Owen Lloyd Davies, Mayor of Haverfordwest and J.P. for the County of Pembroke. The rest of my Father's relatives I am afraid are just names to me.

Of my Mother's relatives I know more for I lived amongst them. My great grandfather, George Goodwin of Ironbridge I remember very distinctly. He built and lived at 'The Terrace' but my grandmother was born at the 'Wharfage' at the house next to the Cooperative Stores. He owned a number of barges plying on the Severn and I am told was usually spoken of as 'Owner Goodwin'. He was a fine big man, well over six feet in height and of an imposing appearance, dark and swarthy, though when I knew him he had a thick mass of snow-white hair. I never saw him without a white or light coloured linen waistcoat, I never remember seeing him with an overcoat and I never remember meeting him without receiving a 'tip'. He was a great fisherman, keen on salmon fishing at a time when salmon were plentiful in the Severn. Many Sunday afternoons I walked up with my Father to spend at my gt. grandfather's house. It is curious my recollections should be so keen and extensive for I was only born in 1871 and he died in 1876.

His first wife Marion (or Mary Ann) Manuel, my great grandmother was a Jewess of Spanish descent. She died at the age of (I think 24) after the birth of her youngest child John. Her father's name I don't know. Her mother who married secondly some one named Griffiths – called Major Griffiths but I expect more probably Sergt. Major – kept a public house in Shrewsbury. She had an only sister who made a runaway match with a wealthy man called 'Dobeggin' or some such name for my grandmother gave the name several pronunciations (Daubeney was one). She never again ever communicated with the family although she stayed in after years at the 'Raven' in Shrewsbury in passing through the town. Her identity I have never discovered. The two sisters were extremely beautiful and my great grandmother has certainly stamped her Jewish ancestry on her descendants. None of us are fair. Some of us are distinctly Jewish in appearance. My great grandmother's marriage was a runaway one – she is buried in a Christian churchyard, and as far as I could ascertain none of her children ever came into contact with any of their mother's people. I know little about her. My grandmother could only tell me she was a remarkably good horsewoman and that my great grandfather's second wife deliberately destroyed every portrait of her that was in existence.

Something of romance entered also into the second marriage of my great grandfather many years after. He was going by coach to Shrewsbury and had entered into conversation with a fellow passenger a Miss Cross. Her people were I think farmers at Leighton or something of the kind. At any rate my own recollection runs to the visits with eggs and poultry on market day of a certain 'Jane Cross' who was by way of being some kind of relative who I had a vague impression was looked down upon. Jane was a garrulous old woman. During that Coach journey the Coach overturned on Leighton Bank and Miss Cross was injured. She became a cripple for life – But my grand-father pursued the acquaintance and from calling 'to enquire' eventually married the lady. What his life was with her I don't know. My grandmother spoke very bitterly of her step- mother and the certain fact remains, the chief fact, I admit which interests me, that whilst my great grand-father was at one time a very wealthy man his second wife beggared him by her wild extravagances. One particular weakness of hers was the distribution of charity. She was a cripple unable to walk but she had a bag always beside her full of money and anyone applying for money got it. On one occasion she gave away £40 in a single day in small change and it was a common occurrence for the same people in different clothes to be 'relieved' several times in the same day. At her death my great grandfather found himself at the end of his money. He married a third time Sarah Geary, then a widow Mrs Harrington. The Harringtons were Bankers in London – her people had

some interest or other in a rope-making business in Broseley. She brought him some money and helped him to save. What money we now have is due to her. I remember her well – but my only recollection of her is seeing her at 'The Terrace' seated on the opposite side of the fireplace to my gt. Grandfather whom she only survived some five or six weeks. I remember seeing them both in their coffins. Both were buried at Madeley in the same grave as my own great grandmother. The second wife lies alone in Leighton churchyard.

He had by his first wife three children. Hannah – my grandmother, William and John. William came to London having married Sarah Boycott – a sister of my godfather Henry Boycott of the Firs. Henry Boycott's daughter, Florence, married Dr Thomas Law-Webb, a brother of Captain Matthew Webb the celebrated swimmer to whom my Father introduced me on the Sunday after he had swam the Channel when he turned up at Coalbrookdale Church. Matt. Webb was taught to swim by my father-in-law Septimus Crookes. As a bachelor in London for some months I lived at the boarding house kept by the widow of Matt Webb and I met both his son Matt and his daughter Nell – at that time an extraordinarily pretty child.

William had a large family but the only one I ever met was William Henry his eldest son whom as Willie Goodwin I knew well both at Coalbrookdale and in London. He is a Chartered Accountant and married a very good-looking woman 'Mary Ellen Louise Prettiform Beccles' a daughter of Judge Beccles – a West Indian and a niece of Bishop Beccles. Willie Goodwin is a very good sort dominated by his wife. They have had a large family of whom the only survivors are Wilfred who has gone into the Church and Claud a good-looking Solicitor in whom the Jewish ancestry is strikingly marked as it was in his sister 'Nella'

John Goodwin my Grandmother's younger brother was a hopeless drunken wastrel. It is said he was never sober for a consecutive week from the time he was 16 till he died and this is very likely true. He lived at Ironbridge but it was not until we were well on to being grown up that we were allowed to know he was a relation. He had a crippled and withered arm – the result of a nurse's negligence and only one eye. The other he lost through a stone flung at him and locally he was known as 'Lord Nelson' by reason of his infirmity. In his earlier life his father found him work of one kind and another but he was a hopeless drunken failure and two houses and a small income were settled on him under my great grandfather's Will. Whereafter he lived the life of a gentleman at large usually spending his time fishing in the Severn.

He was a great trial to my grandmother and my Mother. He married his father's cook and socially sank to her level and I believe was quite happy in it. By her he had ten children – 9 sons and one daughter. I never saw the daughter but the sons were all very good-looking, one or two handsome as Greek Gods. One son enlisted in the Army and led quite a decent life but of the other eight I believe every one appeared before the Magistrates for something or other and most of them 'did time' for poaching or other offences. One of them with some of his pals in a fight very nearly killed a policeman and one was drowned in the Severn in attempting to evade arrest after a poaching expedition. The daughter, after having an illegitimate baby married a lawyer's clerk called Page and altogether the whole family were like their father a hopeless lot. A few weeks sufficed for all of them to squander the reservations under my great grandfather's Will. One thing I can put to their credit – one grandson Arthur enlisted in the Shropshire Territorials and fought in the Anglo-German War.

It was quite a usual occurrence when my grandfather John Fox was on the Bench that he had to retire because one or other of the Goodwins was before the Bench for trial. I remember that on such occasions after conviction the police used always solemnly to describe these disreputable relations of ours as 'well connected'. One of the sons died in his father's lifetime so that the Trust for their benefit under my great grandfather's Will survived for many years until his son came of age in, I think about 1912 when he was paid off and the Trust closed and all communication with that branch of the family finally came to an end – much to my relief.

My grandmother Hannah Goodwin the eldest child and only daughter married my grandfather John Fox at St. Julian's Church in Shrewsbury. His best man was Joseph Almond who was in some way a relative of my wife's family. My grandfather was a son of Richard Fox of Coalbrookdale and his wife Eleanor Griffiths. Richard Fox was the son of William Fox, a farmer at Ashley by his wife Martha Pickstock. She was the daughter of William Pickstock and his wife Martha Smallwood. The Smallwoods were a family of some position living at Snape Hall near Ashley which was at that time their property.

Richard Fox was the first of us to be employed by the Darbys, the firm was afterwards The Coalbrookdale Company Ltd. He – my great grandfather – my grandfather, John Fox – my Father, my brother and myself – four generations of us all did service at Coalbrookdale. My grandfather and after him my Mother and my Aunt held a considerable sum in debentures in the Company.

My great grandfather Richard Fox of course I never knew. He died long before I was born and is buried in Coalbrookdale Churchyard. His wife Eleanor Griffiths I never saw. There have been a number of stories told in Coalbrookdale as to who she was – chief amongst which is a story that she was the daughter of some people named Williams. The real truth is that Eleanor Griffiths was an illegitimate child. Whether my grandfather really knew who her parents were I don't know. At any rate I do not nor does my Mother. My Mother remembers her well and describes her as, a domineering old woman, of a very violent temper. Truth to tell her portrait gives that impression. My Mother has both furniture and china that belonged to the old girl.

Richard and Eleanor Fox had a number of children. My grandfather was the eldest son. His brothers William and Henry I never saw or knew. The former died unmarried in Coalbrookdale. The latter married and died somewhere else – I think somewhere in Staffordshire. There were three daughters Hannah, Anne and Helen. Hannah, the eldest was my Godmother. She always within my recollection lived with my grandfather. I was her favourite and she several times told me she intended to leave me all her money. But I once offended her quite unintentionally, and in the end I shared equally with my brothers and sisters. There are stories from many quarters that in early life she was a very pretty girl. She was a dear old soul but when I knew her there was little to lead one to so imagine. But she was a kindly personage and we all liked and loved her.

My Aunt Anne was much more independent. She obtained the position of postmistress at Coalbrookdale and stuck it till she got her pensions. Then she retired to a small cottage and lived her life in affluent independence until her death at a good old age leaving some hundreds to be divided between my brothers and sisters and myself and the Casleys. She was not pretty, she had none of the attractive vivacity of her elder sister but she played the game and independently supported herself and left some money behind. Both she and her sister are buried at Coalbrookdale.

The youngest daughter Helen, who at the time I write is still alive, married her cousin, William Blagg. He did many things in his life and always made money but he was a restless individual and in their married life – which I don't think was a very happy one – they lived in some 22 or 23 different houses. I remember going to stay with them at Audlem in Cheshire but I remember them best during the few years they lived in Coalbrookdale and farmed 'Westminster Farm'. They only had two children Harry and Alfred. Harry and his father didn't get on any too well – the trouble in the end turning on his choice of occupation, he joined the RMAC and served throughout the Egyptian Campaign. He afterwards went to the USA and died there unmarried. Alfred who has stayed at home and latterly 'lived on his means' – in reality on the joint annuity on the lives of his mother and himself in which under his Will my Uncle's property was sunk – has not made much of a success of his life. He is married – for some reason which no one has ever fathomed he and his wife went through the excitement of a wholly unnecessary midnight elopement – but he has no children. He and his wife separated many years ago. Truth to tell I don't blame her, but I never saw her and who she was and what has become of her I don't think I ever knew. Alfred is a weird sought of individual. My brothers are the Executors of my Uncle's Will and I fancy it has given them a good deal of trouble. Helen, Mrs Blagg is of course my great aunt and great great aunt to my children. Moyra has seen her but I don't think remembers her, but it certainly must be rare for anyone to possess a great great aunt.

There was an old workman – William Hickman – at one time employed by my great grandfather, George Goodwin, who afterwards worked for my grandfather, John Fox and for my Mother. In the end he became a kind of pensioner of my Mother's and died well on in his eighties. The last time I saw him was perhaps twelve months before he died when, hearing I was at Coalbrookdale with Moyra, then a baby; he came over specially to see my daughter and reminded us he had known my great grandfather. Thus at any rate he knew five generations of us and very likely knew my great great grandfather as well.

One other sister my grandfather had, Jane Mrs Barnett – I never knew her or her husband and know little about them but my cousins I saw frequently – Margaret and Agnes were nuns. The former at the Convent of the Sacred Heart at Highgate where she died a few years ago and where I often saw her. Agnes is the Superior of a Convent of the same Order at Buenos Aires. I saw her once when the business of the Order brought her on a visit to Highgate. But I remember them both before they became nuns. It would be difficult to imagine a happier person than Margaret as I remember her at the Convent. She loved the place and her life and her work. Their only brother, Charlie, I often saw. For many years prior to his marriage he came pretty regularly every summer to stay either at my grandfather's house or at ours. We all of us liked him immensely – I remember his marriage and have met his wife. If I remember rightly she was rather a pretty woman. But it brings the passage of years home to one to think that his two sons are now serving His Majesty during the War. Charlie is a Chartered Accountant. He inherited some money and his wife also had money

Bibliography

Debrett's Peerage Baronetage and Knightage, London, 1926

Eve G.W. *Heraldry as Art*, Batsford, London, 1907

Ex Libris Journal, Plymouth, 1893–1908

Fairbairn James *Crests of Great Britain and Ireland*, Tuttle, Vermont, USA 1968

Fox-Davies A.C. *A Complete Guide to Heraldry*, Revised edition, London, 1985

Fox-Davies A.C. *Armorial Families*, 7 Editions, 1895–1930, Edinburgh

Fox-Davies A.C. *The Art of Heraldry*, Bloomsbury Books, London 1986

Fox-Davies A.C. *The Book of Public Arms*, first edition, 1893, T.C. and E.C. Jack

Fox-Davies A.C. *The Book of Public Arms*, second edition, 1915, Edinburgh

Genealogical Magazine, 1895–1906, London

Kelly's Handbook to the Titled, Landed and Official Classes, London, 1935

Joslin E.C. *Standard Catalogue of British Orders and Decorations*, third edition, London, 1976

Lee B.N. *Some Recollections of a Bookplate Collector*, The Bookplate Society, London, 1988

Lee B.N. *Some Bookplates of Heralds*, The Bookplate Society, London, 2003

Vinycomb, John *On the Processes for the Production of Ex Libris*, 1894

Who was Who, Vol. I, 1893–1915, A. and C. Black, London

Who was Who, Vol. II, 1916–27, A. and C. Black, London

Who was Who, Vol. III, 1928–40, A. and C. Black, London

'X' (Fox-Davies A.C.) *The Right to Bear Arms*, Elliot Stock, London, 1899

Index

A list of plate owners in alphabetical order

This edition is limited to four hundred and fifty
copies of which two hundred and fifty
are for members of The Bookplate Society.
Thirty are special copies, hard bound,
containing original tipped in bookplates
and signed and numbered I–XXX.
The remainder are for public sale.

This is the members' book of The Bookplate Society
for the years 2011 and 2012

Text © Colin R. Lattimore

Published by The Bookplate Society, 2012

ISBN 978-0-9555428-2-4

Images scanned by Geoffrey Vevers

Copy-editing by Peter Youatt

Design and formatting by James Shurmer

Printed by Henry Ling Limited at the Dorset Press,
Dorchester DT1 1HD

The Bookplate Society is an international society
of collectors, bibliophiles, artists and others
dedicated to promoting bookplate use and study.
For details of publications and membership
benefits, see page 140 of this book and also visit
The Bookplate Society's website:
www.bookplatesociety.org

The Bookplate Society

An international society of collectors, bibliophiles, artists, and others dedicated to promoting bookplate study

About The Bookplate Society

Bookplates, also known as ex-libris, have since the 15th century been placed in books to declare ownership. Many artists, some famous such as William Hogarth, Aubrey Beardsley and John Piper, have designed bookplates, and many celebrated people (e.g. Samuel Pepys and Rudyard Kipling) have used them, but a personal bookplate has been available to anyone owning a library and wishing to place in the books a printed design as a mark of possession. You can still acquire bookplates of all ages and styles, and in a gathering of reasonable size there may be found some interesting and even scarce items.

Founded in 1972, The Bookplate Society is the direct descendant of the world's first such organisation, the Ex Libris Society, 1891–1908, and its creation and successor, the Bookplate Exchange Club. Our purpose is to encourage the production, use, collecting, and study of bookplates. We achieve this through our publications, lectures, visits to collections, members' auctions, social meetings, and exhibitions.

We focus on British bookplates, but our membership is worldwide. Some of our members are bookplate artists and we maintain a list of British designers who are currently willing to accept commissions. Many of our subscribers are not bookplate collectors at all, but have diverse interests in the kindred fields of heraldry, genealogy, printing, the art of the book, bibliography, engraving, graphic art, and family and local history. They find the range of bookplate design, technique and history fascinating.

For fuller information visit: **www.bookplatesociety.org**

Membership Benefits

The annual subscription of £30 (£39 outside the UK; or $65 or €50) payable on 1 January each year gives these benefits:

The Bookplate Journal (ISSN 0264-3693) is published in Spring and Autumn each year. In 2003 *The Bookplate Journal* commenced its second series in a new, enlarged format. The substantial articles cover well-researched essays, bookplates of individuals and families, checklists of artists (contemporary and historical), collectors and collecting, notes & queries, book reviews etc.

The Bookplate Society Newsletter (ISSN 0309-7935) appears twice a year in Summer and Winter. It gives news of meetings, auction lists, membership changes, sales and wants, and items of interest not covered in *The Bookplate Journal*.

Every two years, members receive a book. Our members' book for 2009/10 was *The Bookplates and Badges of C.F.A. Voysey* by Karen Livingstone, 304 pages, hardback, published by Antique Collectors' Club in association Crab Tree Farm Foundation. We have an ongoing plan to publish studies of the work of artists, and to cover bookplate history by styles, themes and by different areas of the British Isles.

Each year the Society holds a bookplate study meeting and/or a visit to a bookplate collection. Two other meetings take the form of bookplate auctions, in which many members participate keenly by post or e-mail.

Please address membership enquiries to **members@bookplatesociety.org** or write to the Membership Secretary, 32 Belitha Villas, London N1 1PD.

Bookplate Society Publications

Some recent titles in print are shown below (prices to members in brackets). A full list appears on the Society's website. Postage is extra and will be quoted on request to: **publications@bookplatesociety.org**

BOOKPLATES BY EDMUND HORT NEW
Brian North Lee 98 pages, 1999. (£10) £15

SOME NORFOLK AND SUFFOLK EX-LIBRIS
John Blatchly 154 pages, 2000. (£15) £22

PREMIUM OR PRIZE EX-LIBRIS
Brian North Lee 118 pages, 2001. (£13) £20

BOOKPLATES OF GEORGE WOLFE PLANK
John Blatchly 96 pages, 2002. (£10) £16

SOME BOOKPLATES OF HERALDS
Brian North Lee 155 pages, 2003. (£14) £20

PAROCHIAL LIBRARY EX-LIBRIS
Brian North Lee 136 pages, 2004. (£10) £16

BOOKPLATES IN THE TROPHY STYLE
Paul Latcham 184 pages, 2005. (£14) £20

SCOTTISH BOOKPLATES
Brian N. Lee & Ilay Campbell 144 pages, 2006. (£14) £20

EAST ANGLIAN EX-LIBRIS
John Blatchly 128 pages, 2008. (£14) £18